Dead Endplay

A Pemberton Mystery   Ken Allan

MASTER POINT PRESS • TORONTO, CANADA

Master Point Press
331 Douglas Ave.
Toronto, Ontario, Canada, M5M 1H2
(416)781-0351   Email: info@masterpointpress.com
Websites: www.masterpointpress.com
             www.teachbridge.com
             www.bridgeblogging.com
             www.ebooksbridge.com

Library and Archives Canada Cataloguing in Publication

Allan, Ken, 1940-
Deadly endplay : a Pemberton Bridge Club mystery / Ken Allan.

Also issued in electronic formats.
ISBN 978-1-897106-68-6
            I. Title.

PS8601.L42778D42 2011   C813'.6   C2011-901586-2

We acknowledge the financial support of the Government of Canada through the Book Publishing Industry Development Program (BPIDP) for our publishing activities.

Editor	Suzanne Hocking
Interior format	Sally Sparrow
Cover and interior design	Olena S. Sullivan/New Mediatrix

1 2 3 4 5 6 7   15 14 13 12 11
PRINTED IN CANADA

ACKNOWLEDGMENTS

This book evolved over a period of about thirty years, until I had a small number of copies printed in 2008. The manuscript was read at various stages by Don Kersey, Paddy Allan, Mark and Shona Donovan. They made numerous suggestions to make the final draft much better. The evolution has continued. This is much the same story, but now it is told somewhat better as a result of feedback from readers, reviewers and, especially, many suggestions to improve the flow of the story from Ray Lee and Suzanne Hocking.

Special thanks to Joy Allan and Bert Weir for the physical appearance of that first version of this book.

Ian Fleming, in *Moonraker*, has James Bond deal the following bridge hand to the villain, Hugo Drax:

♠ A K Q J
♡ A K Q J
◇ A K
♣ K J 9

You could play a lifetime without holding a hand this rich in high cards. Drax accepts it as his due, doubles Bond's grand slam in clubs and doesn't suspect he is being swindled until it becomes apparent that he is not going to take a single trick. The hands of Bond and his partner are:

M	Bond
♠ 10 9 8 7	♠ —
♡ 6 5 4 3	♡ —
◇ —	◇ Q 8 7 6 5 4 3 2
♣ 7 6 5 3 2	♣ A Q 10 8 4

This is a variant of a famous whist hand (the Duke of Cumberland's hand) and while it helps, in following the action, to know a little about bridge (or whist), you don't have to know much about cards to appreciate that Drax has a pretty good hand and that it would be unusual, not to mention deflating (and, when the high stakes have just been doubled and redoubled, expensive) to lose with such a hand.

It is very unusual to find a bridge hand in a popular novel. Bridge slows down the narrative and there are very few deals where the effect of the bidding and the play on the characters is as easily understood as with Drax and Bond.

Bridge deals and storytelling are an uneasy fit. Some writers of bridge novels avoid bridge deals entirely in the hope that they can reach a larger audience. Some bridge players could follow the bidding and play if they encountered a bridge deal in a novel, but generally choose not to read such novels.

And yet... and yet... bridge hands get under your skin. Some players exhibit a personality when they are playing bridge that is quite different from their personality away from the table. The same hand can provoke quite different responses depending on the personality of the player. This has practical implications in bidding and play. Recognizing and making use of the way different personality types respond to bridge deals is the main subject of the bridge classic *Why You Lose at Bridge* by S.J. Simon. Likewise, in *Bridge in the Menagerie*, the peerless Victor Mollo uses personality traits to bring about unexpected and entertaining twists in the play of bridge deals. Both authors are fun to read. Both write about characters that can be found in every bridge club. Both have characters that can be defined by a single stroke of the pen. Both authors stay pretty much at the bridge table.

Duplicate bridge players seldom leave bridge behind when they leave the table. They always have a story to tell if asked about interesting or challenging hands, and they spend time thinking about triumphs and disasters when they should be doing something else. The rare exceptions are players who play the game purely to relax and who expend very little mental energy on the game. In this novel, Russell and Doc are such characters, but they are unusual in that respect and even they are not impervious.

This novel takes place in a fictional town wedged into an actual landscape located north of Bruce Mines and east of Sault Ste. Marie. The story is a mystery of sorts, but with just one serious suspect, it is not a whodunit. It is more of a whether-anyone-dunit and, if so, howdunit.

S.J. Simon concentrated on four personality types. The average bridge club has many more than that. Appendix A (p. 213) has a short description of the Pemberton Duplicate Bridge Club members who appear most often.

CHAPTER 1

THE PEMBERTON CHRONICLE

Friday, November 26, 1982

THE JAY'S NEST

by Jane Seabrook

South dealer
Neither Vul.

North (Corey)
♠ K 10 9
♡ K 5 4
◇ K Q 10 3
♣ 6 5 2

West (Kit)
♠ Q 5 4 2
♡ Q 2
◇ A J 9 5
♣ 9 8 4

East (Jake)
♠ 7 3
♡ 10 8 7 6 3
◇ 7 4 2
♣ K J 3

South (Jay)
♠ A J 8 6
♡ A J 9
◇ 8 6
♣ A Q 10 7

West	North	East	South
			1NT
pass	3NT	all pass	

Opening lead: ◇5

This was the second hand out of the box. On the first board our opponents, Kit and Jake, got a top because I made a mistake on defense and let them make a game contract that nobody else was in.

"I was pushy," said Kit to Jake, "but I knew you'd play it well."

What he meant was that Corey and I could be counted on to defend poorly. Honestly, these experts assume that anyone who is inferior to them at bridge is too dumb to understand when they talk in code.

The second hand cheered me up a little. I could see right away there were finesses all over the place and I just love finesses. The experts say a finesse should be taken only as a last resort but I'll leave them to their strips and squeezes — just show me a finesse and I'll take it. I won the diamond lead with the king in dummy and led a club, finessing the ten, which held, and I got that warm feeling you get when you just know everything is where you want it to be. I led a spade to the ten, which won. Bliss. Then I noticed there was a two-way finesse in spades — if the spade queen had been on my right, I should have finessed toward my hand rather than toward the dummy.

It was a good thing I didn't see it sooner or I would have gotten it wrong. As much as I love finesses, I hate two-way finesses. With the simple finesse, you just take it and if it wins you get an extra trick and if it loses... well you were never going to win that trick anyway so it doesn't matter. With two-way finesses, there is a right way and a wrong way. With an unerring sense of misdirection, you can go wrong every time.

Fran says if there is no other indication, two-way finesses should be taken toward the longer hand. I'm sure she gave a reason but I forgot it long ago. The catch in this is the 'no other indication.' I'm not sure I would recognize an 'indication' even if there was one. Finessing toward the dummy was backward, sort of, but it was right this time so who cares — besides Kit, of course. He sat there squirming and I could tell he was not enjoying this hand, which cheered me up no end. Maybe the 'indication' was that I wanted to get back over to dummy to finesse in clubs again so I might as well take the two-way finesse in the direction that was most convenient for my plan.

Still, if I had noticed the two-way spade finesse I would have gotten it wrong. It was a narrow escape, but I didn't let it slow me down. A club to the queen and a spade to the nine got me two more extra tricks. With every successful finesse, I was enjoying myself more and more. I cashed dummy's spade king and played to my club ace, leaving me in my hand with these cards left.

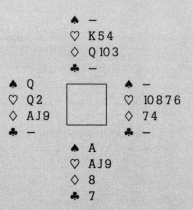

Next I played a diamond toward the diamond queen in dummy and when Kit went up with the ace, I was almost ready to forgive him. Kit returned a spade to my ace. I was about to lead small to the heart king when I had an inspiration — maybe I should take the heart finesse backward too. So I played the heart jack and as soon as Kit covered with the queen I realized that I had acted too quickly. The finesse had worked, but I didn't have an extra trick. When a finesse works, it's supposed to give you an extra trick. That's one of the rules of bridge!

Then I saw there was another finesse available in hearts — with the king, queen and jack gone, and the ace-nine in my hand, I now had a finesse against the ten. This is what I love about bridge. Just when the deal seems to be over, another finesse appears out of thin air. I was pretty sure my club seven was good, but there was no need to take a chance. I just pitched it on the queen of diamonds and took the heart finesse.

There were only two other players to make three overtricks on this deal, so Corey and I had a tie for top.

Kit Know-It-All McCrea was fit to be tied, muttering about practice finesses, but I figured a bottom served him right after what he had said. I told him "You buttered your bread, Kit, now lie in it."

He just stared at me with a blank look on his face. Honestly, I don't think he understood a word I said. It's just amazing how some people can be so good at bridge and so bad at life.

CHAPTER

On a cool Tuesday evening in late April, 1983, a blue cloud of smoke hung over fifteen tables of bridge players in the Elks Hall. In ten years, the club, like other duplicate bridge clubs across North America, would become non-smoking. Until then, a smoker could light up at will, inhale deeply while studying the cards, and then, ready to proceed, place the cigarette in an ashtray, the smoke wafting lovingly toward the player at the table who was most offended by secondhand smoke.

When the Methodists of Pemberton sold their church to the Benevolent and Protective Order of Elks in 1925, they had no idea that it would become a home for instruments of the devil. The game of Contract Bridge had just been invented, so they couldn't know that, in twenty years, Contract Bridge would be the favorite indoor pastime of the citizens of Pemberton. Not on Sundays, of course, though in another twenty years their grandchildren, feeling a little wicked, would play bridge even on Sundays.

This evening, sixty bridge players sat at fifteen tables arranged in two rows down the length of the hall. The players were a cross-section of Pemberton. Women outnumbered men by two to one and over-fifties outnumbered under-fifties by the same margin. Beyond those two broad distinctions, there was no discernible type, with all ages and occupations represented.

The youngest members were Kevin Crockford and Barry Penrose, who looked like teenagers but were actually in their early twenties. Both worked at the Brickworks for several years after graduating from high school and were now commuting to Algoma College in the Soo.

The oldest were Jenny Bird and Carrie Hamel, both over ninety, who lived at the Red Castle retirement home (red brick donated by the Brickworks). They were picked up and delivered back after the game by Jenny's nephew, Jim Campbell, better known as the Professor.

Although most of the field was experienced and fairly good at the game, even ordinary looking deals could produce a variety of results. Take Board 15:

South dealer
N-S Vul.

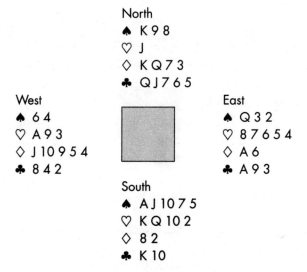

North
♠ K 9 8
♡ J
♢ K Q 7 3
♣ Q J 7 6 5

West
♠ 6 4
♡ A 9 3
♢ J 10 9 5 4
♣ 8 4 2

East
♠ Q 3 2
♡ 8 7 6 5 4
♢ A 6
♣ A 9 3

South
♠ A J 10 7 5
♡ K Q 10 2
♢ 8 2
♣ K 10

The cards in this board were shuffled and dealt at Table 8 at the beginning of the evening. On the face of it, there was nothing very unusual about the deal. Looking at all four hands, it is surely routine to bid the four-spade game, taking ten tricks (losing just three aces — a simple spade finesse avoids losing a trump trick to the queen of spades). Despite this, in actual play, not everyone would get to the same contract or take the same number of tricks. In fact, this straightforward deal got varied treatment both in the bidding and in the play. Not only that, it was, for several players, the deal of the night. Indeed, for a few others, this deal started small ripples that would never completely fade away.

When Board 15 arrived at Table 4, Katie Burton and Corey Loucks bid confidently to four spades. Katie was a buxom woman in her mid-forties who wore her red hair up in a bun from which a strand or two was always making an escape. She had been a regular duplicate player for six years, starting soon after David's heart attack made her a widow (David was the Burton of Burton & Johnson Realty). A rubber bridge player for all of her adult life, Katie found, when she took up duplicate, that her bridge skills were inferior to those of the other players in the club. She took the Professor's advanced class in card play several times and absorbed a little bit more each time. She was gradually becoming a competent player, much better than her rubber bridge friends, but barely average in the duplicate club.

West led the jack of diamonds and Corey laid down her cards, making Katie responsible for winning ten or more tricks from their combined hands.

Dummy (Corey)
♠ K 9 8
♡ J
♢ K Q 7 3
♣ Q J 7 6 5

South (Katie)
♠ A J 10 7 5
♡ K Q 10 2
♢ 8 2
♣ K 10

Katie won the second round of diamonds in dummy and paused to consider how she should play the trump suit. With just two top honors, she would have to hope the missing spade queen was on her right. Should she play the king first before leading low toward her hand for the finesse? Or should she hold the king in reserve to get back to dummy to finesse a second time in case Rose, on her right, started with four spades? No need for that — with the nine in dummy she could play the king first, in case the queen dropped, and then run the nine.

Eyeing the spade nine, Katie suddenly realized she could also finesse toward the dummy. This was what the Professor called a two-way finesse — if the queen was on her right, she should finesse toward her hand as she had been planning; however, if the queen was on her left, she should finesse toward dummy. Katie hated two-way finesses.

Katie's attention drifted to the other suits. The clubs would be solid once she forced out the ace. The hearts too. Suddenly the jack of hearts in the dummy leapt into sharp focus. It almost grinned at her as she made a connection between the hand in front of her and an advanced play she knew only in theory. Top players make such connections regularly, but Katie had difficulty transferring theory to the table unless it was a situation that occurred frequently. For Katie, this moment, when abstract theory shone its light on an actual hand, was an epiphany. Unless she was missing something, she had all the ingredients for Clayton Carmichael's pseudo endplay!

It had been two months since Clayton explained how it worked. Then for several weeks she had been on the lookout. Now, at last, she could solve a nasty two-way finesse by making an expert play. The key was the singleton jack of hearts in dummy. She said, "Heart, please." Jake Harden, on her left, won with the ace, and Katie held her breath.

Jake, in his late forties, had weathered skin from years of exposure to sun and wind on his mixed farm north of Pemberton. He should have looked older than his age. In fact, he had a boyishness that made him look younger. He spread his cards with labor-thickened fingers and tried to figure out why Katie Burton was so tense. It looked as though she wanted to trump a couple of hearts in dummy, so the marked play was to lead a trump and hope that his partner held the ace — a spade return would cut her down to one ruff. Perhaps she was hoping he wouldn't lead a trump. Or maybe it was just that leaving the kiddies on the street made her nervous.

After deliberating for an interminable length of time, Jake lead a spade to the nine, queen and Katie's ace. "Won't Clayton be pleased," she said, beaming at the confounded Jake Harden.

"What's he got to do with it?" asked Jake.

His irritation was lost on Katie. "I just can't wait to tell him how I did his pseudo endplay," she said as she drew trumps, knocked out the club ace and claimed the rest of the tricks.

The full deal, once again:

South dealer
N-S Vul.

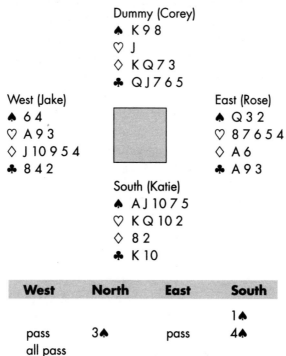

Dummy (Corey)
♠ K 9 8
♡ J
♢ K Q 7 3
♣ Q J 7 6 5

West (Jake)
♠ 6 4
♡ A 9 3
♢ J 10 9 5 4
♣ 8 4 2

East (Rose)
♠ Q 3 2
♡ 8 7 6 5 4
♢ A 6
♣ A 9 3

South (Katie)
♠ A J 10 7 5
♡ K Q 10 2
♢ 8 2
♣ K 10

West	North	East	South
			1♠
pass	3♠	pass	4♠
all pass			

Opening lead: ◊J

Jake looked around the room of duplicate bridge players and saw Clayton sitting South, eight tables away. He checked his card: five rounds had been played. "Don't tell him until after the game," he said, "He'll be playing this hand on the last round."

Jim Campbell was Pemberton's bridge teacher. One of his first students, back in the 1960s, had referred to him as The Professor. The name stuck and was now used even by citizens of Pemberton who were unaware that he taught bridge. He was actually a stationary engineer. In the course of a shift at the Brickworks, where he was in charge of the steam plant and kilns, he might become covered with grease, dust and cobwebs, but he was always immaculate when he strolled out of the Brickworks at 4:45 p.m., wearing a tweed jacket with leather on the elbows and smoking a pipe.

He was a good teacher. In fact, he was somewhat better as a teacher than as a player. He had rules for every situation and they were good rules. But rules have exceptions and bridge rules seem to have more than their share. The Professor knew this, but was not good at spotting the exceptions, especially at the table. On the hand that had given Katie Burton such extraordinary pleasure, he opened the bidding with one spade. Rita responded two clubs, the Professor bid two hearts and Rita jumped to game in spades. The opening lead was the diamond jack.

Dummy (Rita)
♠ K 9 8
♡ J
♦ K Q 7 3
♣ Q J 7 6 5

South (Professor)
♠ A J 10 7 5
♡ K Q 10 2
♦ 8 2
♣ K 10

It was obvious that he was going to cover the diamond jack with dummy's queen, but the Professor stopped to analyze the lead and make a plan. Making a plan was the rule most widely disregarded by his students. Most of them liked the action of play so much that they refused to do any thinking until they encountered a problem. The Professor could see that with three aces to lose, the only problem was to decide how to take the two-way finesse in spades. His rule for two-way decisions was to make them the same way every time — then you could be sure of being right half the time. For two-way finesses one could adopt a completely arbitrary rule like always playing toward dummy, or geographical north, or the biggest person at the table. His personal solution in this case was to adopt the rubber bridge rule that the queen lay over the jack.

In rubber bridge, the queen would often cover the jack (but seldom the other way around) in the play to a trick. The queen would go into the deck just under the jack and during an imperfect shuffle the two cards would stay together. During the deal, the queen would be dealt immediately after the jack. None of this applied at duplicate, where players keep their cards in front of them in order to be able to put the hand, as they received it, back into the pocket of the board. It was, he thought, as good as any other arbitrary rule (and it meant that when he played rubber bridge, he didn't have to change his rule). If the queen was over the jack, then it would be in the hand on his left.

Having made a plan, he called for the diamond queen from dummy. This was won by the ace on his right and a diamond was returned to dummy's king. In order to follow his plan for the trump-suit finesse, he had to play from his hand. The Professor crossed to his spade ace. This was an inferior play, something the Professor was quite capable of figuring out. But when he had a rule to follow, he didn't always think things through. He led his jack, losing to the queen on his right. Down one.

When they examined the traveling score slip, it appeared that of the seven times Board 15 had been played so far, there was one other pair in four spades down one trick, one pair in two spades making four, one pair in three notrump (declared from the north side, don't ask about the bidding) making three, and three pairs (including Katie and Corey) in four spades making four. A tie for bottom, so far, for the Professor. "The problem with a weak field," he muttered, "is that most of them don't even notice there's a two-way finesse, so they play toward the long hand, which, this time, just happens to be right."

Russell Hicks was a bear of a man, a tame bear who looked slightly out of place at the bridge table. He enjoyed bridge, but for him it was a much simpler game than for the majority of duplicate players. He liked the rituals of duplicate bridge — the orderly movement of players and boards around the room, fanning a new hand every five to ten minutes, sorting the cards into suits, bidding the hand, playing all thirteen cards one at a time. He gave each hand a minimum of thought and when the last card was played, the hand disappeared from his mind. This was a pleasant, relaxing way to spend an evening as long as he didn't do it too often. Once a week was just right.

Russell was a welder and his lack of application at the bridge table surprised those like Jake Harden who dealt with Russell on a professional basis. Russell was very good at what he did and would typically recognize a piece of equipment he had welded years before. When it came to bridge, however, he could talk about when he played and who he played with but not the cards he held. In comparison with the rest of the people in the room this evening, Russell was not a good player. He had signed up for the Professor's lessons a couple of times, absorbing just enough to get by.

Nevertheless, he sometimes scored better than one would expect from a player who put so little effort into the game. The one bridge play that never failed to get Russell's full attention was the ruff. He always made maximum use of the trump suit and if the success of a contract depended on a cross ruff, there was no one likely to do better.

On Board 15, after dummy's diamond king won the second trick, Russell's first thought was to ruff a diamond. When Russell had a first thought, he seldom wasted time on a second. After the diamond ruff, Russell was in his hand and paused briefly to consider a course of action.

Dummy (Jenny)
♠ K 9 8
♡ J
♢ 7
♣ Q J 7 6 5

South (Russell)
♠ A J 10 7
♡ K Q 10 2
♢ —
♣ K 10

Russell saw that if he lost a heart he could do some more ruffing before he drew trumps. The Professor had tried, in vain, to convince Russell there was no gain in ruffing in the long hand, as Russell had just done when he ruffed the diamond. This deal was going to make the Professor's task even more difficult because Russell was about to take more tricks than the Professor. Of course, once the heart jack forced out the heart ace, there would be no need to ruff hearts. But Russell played a heart before this occurred to him. Kevin, on his left, carelessly played low so the heart jack won the trick! Although this was an unexpected turn of events, Russell knew what to do next. He ruffed another diamond and then ruffed a heart. This brought about the following end position with dummy on lead:

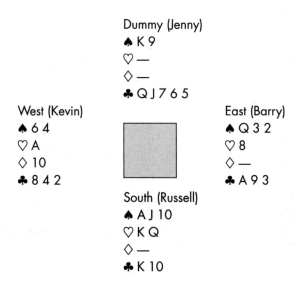

Dummy (Jenny)
♠ K 9
♡ —
♢ —
♣ Q J 7 6 5

West (Kevin)
♠ 6 4
♡ A
♢ 10
♣ 8 4 2

East (Barry)
♠ Q 3 2
♡ 8
♢ —
♣ A 9 3

South (Russell)
♠ A J 10
♡ K Q
♢ —
♣ K 10

Russell called for a small club and craftily dropped his king under Barry's ace. Barry was on lead and considered his options. He correctly guessed that if he played a club, Russell would win and coast home on the crossruff. Barry played a trump, but to no avail, as this was won by Russell's jack. Russell ruffed another heart with the spade king, played dummy's queen and jack of clubs, throwing his last heart (Barry kicking himself for not having discarded clubs on the third and fourth diamond leads), and won the last two tricks with the ten and ace of trumps.

In the bidding, they had stopped short of game (Russell passed Jenny's conservative limit raise — being conservative usually worked best for them), so they didn't have a good board. Russell and Jenny took turns apologizing for not going on. Nevertheless, Russell was pleased with the result. He took one trick more than anybody else and two more than the Professor (the results of everybody who had played the hand were there on the traveling score slip for all to see).

"I don't see how he could go down," said Russell. "Sometimes he gets too fancy."

The Stinson twins (Fran had actually been a Porter for seventeen years now, but whenever she played with her brother she became a Stinson again) were the strongest pair in the club. Outside the bridge club, Phil was quiet and self-effacing. As one of the best players in Pemberton, he was treated with more respect when he played bridge than in any other part of his life. At the bridge table, his bidding and play of the cards spoke for him. Fran was reserved, like her twin brother, but more assertive in social situations and more likely to take control when something needed to be done. As a bridge player, she was more conservative than Phil, more knowledgeable about bridge theory and technically better at playing the hand.

On Board 15, they had the same bidding sequence as the Professor and Rita, making Fran the declarer.

Dummy (Phil)
♠ K 9 8
♡ J
♢ K Q 7 3
♣ Q J 7 6 5

South (Fran)
♠ A J 10 7 5
♡ K Q 10 2
♢ 8 2
♣ K 10

Fran noted the two-way finesse in spades, and that the odds favored taking the finesse from dummy to hand. While for most distributions of the five outstanding spades, an arbitrary rule like the Professor's was completely satisfactory, the Professor's rule did not take into account the possibility that the opposing cards might split 4-1. It was possible for Fran to play dummy's king, protecting against a stiff queen (on her left), and still pick up four to the queen on her right, but not possible to finesse toward the short hand in dummy and still combine these chances.

Fran didn't like taking finesses unless she had to, so she looked for an alternative. There was no need to ruff hearts in dummy, but if she led a heart it would look as though she wanted to do just that; the defender who won the trick might therefore play a trump. This was the play Clayton Carmichael called a pseudo endplay. The objective was to make the defender think there was a danger where none existed. If the ploy succeeded, the imaginary danger of ruffs in the dummy would propel the defender into a course which was truly dangerous for the defense, because leading a trump solved the guess for declarer. Furthermore, if the defender who won the heart trick did not play a trump, it was a good bet that she was avoiding trumps because she had the queen, so you would finesse accordingly.

After winning the second diamond, Fran called for the heart jack from dummy and then played the king from her hand, hoping to create the impression she was missing the heart queen and was trying to steal a trick before beginning a crossruff. The play proceeded much the same as it had at Katie's table (except that Fran had a losing heart deuce to be ruffed in dummy before all the trumps were pulled).

On the last round of the evening, Doc Shaver played against Dan Cogan and Clayton Carmichael. Doc was a short, round man with a white mustache who had been Doc for so long that no one remembered his first name. Widower Clayton Carmichael, declarer on this deal, was a retired financial advisor and a pretty good bridge player. Clayton and Dan bid one spade — two clubs, two hearts — four spades. Doc led his diamond jack and saw the following dummy:

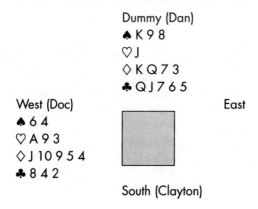

Dummy (Dan)
♠ K 9 8
♡ J
♢ K Q 7 3
♣ Q J 7 6 5

West (Doc)
♠ 6 4
♡ A 9 3
♢ J 10 9 5 4
♣ 8 4 2

East

South (Clayton)

Doc's diamond jack was covered. Daisy won with her ace and returned a diamond to Doc's nine and dummy's king. Clayton gave a grunt of satisfaction and played dummy's heart jack to Doc's ace.

Doc Shaver was not one of the better players in the club despite the fact that he was highly regarded as a doctor and was, as far as anyone could tell, a very intelligent man. He played bridge to relax. There were those who felt that if he ever took the game seriously, he would be very good. The dissenters pointed out that he had been playing for years and he would surely be better by now if he had any potential at all. He was a better player than Russell, but like Russell, he could enjoy an evening of bridge without giving the game his full attention. Like all bridge players, he preferred winning to losing, but he hadn't much experience with winning overall. Tuesday duplicate was, for him, a social event rather than a competition and he was content with an occasional victory on individual hands.

Since there was no future in diamonds and it looked as though Clayton wanted to trump hearts in the dummy, Doc decided to play a spade. As he reached for the spade four, he felt a little tingle in his fingertips. Like the rat in the experiment that has been shocked when it touches a certain lever, Doc associated pain with this situation. If this had happened to another player, the momentum of a considered decision would have carried the spade four into play, but Doc made good decisions as a doctor by heeding similar warning signals, so he stopped and reconsidered.

He did not ordinarily remember hands or bridge situations, but a picture, from a year before, floated up from memory. Clayton's jovial, hail-fellow-well-met, fulsome manner was not ordinarily offensive, but when swollen by a small victory, at your expense, it was quite irritating. Doc remembered, with surprising clarity, a situation like this where he led a trump to prevent ruffs and instead pickled his partner's queen. Clayton's preening and bluff condescension at the time insured that the memory remained intact.

Not liking any of his options, Doc finally played a club. When Clayton got back in, he ran the spade jack, which lost to the queen. Clayton was down one.

CHAPTER 3

It was customary after the game for those who wanted to discuss hands to gather at the Cornerstone. Doc seldom joined the group. but his first appointment for the next day had been cancelled and he knew Dan Cogan and the Stinsons would make a more satisfying audience for his small victory than would his non-bridge-playing wife.

Dan Cogan was an ex-policeman who had played rubber bridge with his wife Connie from the time they were married. He took up duplicate bridge after he and Connie separated. "Have a seat, Doc," called Dan. "It was good to see someone catch Clayton at his own game, even though it cost us first place." Dan described the play on Board 15 with special emphasis on Doc's refusal to cooperate in Clayton's execution of his pseudo endplay.

Clayton, who was usually a regular at the Cornerstone, was absent this evening.

"Just getting my own back," said Doc. "Clayton used that play on me a year ago and it probably would have worked for him again tonight except he was so pleased about it the last time that it stuck with me." The assembled company took turns describing what had happened when they played this deal. "You did well to avoid the trump return," said Jake to the Doc. "Katie set the same trap for me as Clayton set for you and I fell for it. Pleased her no end."

"You know what really surprised me?" said Doc. "Even though Clayton was startled when his play didn't work, he didn't scowl or mutter."

"You have his number," said Phil Stinson. "Clayton hates to lose to anyone who, no offense Doc, he figures isn't as good as he is. That pseudo endplay has got to be his favorite play — he thinks he invented it. Good old Clayton should have gone up in smoke. I wonder where his head was tonight."

When Dan finished an evening of bridge, there were a few deals he remembered in detail and quite a few more he remembered in bits and pieces. After going through the complete set at the Cornerstone, with the aid of the recollections of the other players, he could recall the main features of every deal. This evening, after he left the Cornerstone, the one that kept pushing all others aside was Clayton's hand against Doc.

Dan was annoyed with himself. Doc had been quite right that Clayton's behavior was atypical and Dan should have noticed. Especially since Dan had been conscious of something off about Clayton ever since Elsie's death. In the small police department of Pemberton, most of Dan's work was routine. When detective work was called for, Dan showed an aptitude that led to him becoming the department sleuth. He paid attention to the smallest details and was good at spotting the detail that was out of place. This is also a useful mental attitude for a bridge player to develop.

Card sense and concentration on small details go a long way to making a good bridge player. The best bridge players also have a strong desire to win. All in good measure, of course. An excessive desire to win can affect judgment and clarity. Dan knew he and Clayton were having a good game and that two good boards against the Doc on the last round would have given them a good shot at placing first. His irritation with Clayton for going down in four spades kept him from noticing Clayton's lack of reaction to being misled by the Doc. Not that Dan normally got upset when his partner was deceived. It was just that in this case the situation was clear.

The problem was that Clayton had turned his pseudo endplay into a formula and followed the formula even when there was evidence that this was an exception. Dan knew that Doc did not have the spade queen. The Doc was a deliberate player who never made a decision quickly unless it was an obvious one. When Clayton played the heart jack to Doc's ace, the obvious play, even for an average player like the Doc, would be a trump back to cut down on the ruffs. When Doc started to play almost immediately, Dan was certain that Doc was going to make the obvious play of a trump. Then Doc stopped and thought for almost a minute, and Dan did some thinking too, even though, as dummy, he could do no more than observe. Dan suspected that Clayton was up to his favorite trick. If that was the case, then a failure by Doc to play trump should signal that he had something to protect in spades — hence Clayton would assume that the Doc had the spade queen.

When Doc returned a club, Dan was convinced that he had been going to play a trump and that it was not the possession of the queen that had stopped him; with the spade queen, a trump return would not have been obvious, so Doc would have been much slower in reaching that first aborted decision. Clayton had gone to the well once too often — the Doc had been burned and would sooner give up some ruffs than give Clayton another chance to gloat over his pseudo endplay. The Doc was refusing to play ball, but he had not done it smoothly enough. Clayton should have noticed that reversal on Doc's part. If Clayton had been awake, they would have had a good board instead of a tie for bottom.

Clayton was popular, especially with the novices. He loved an audience and would regale them with tales of his exploits. Other good players were willing to help anyone who had a question about a hand, but there was no one as outgoing as Clayton. On the other hand, when weak players came to his table, Clayton expected tops and felt he was being denied his just deserts when they did not oblige. Especially galling for him was to have a weak player make a bad play which worked out well because of an unusual lie of the cards or, worst of all, because it induced Clayton to make a wrong assumption. On such occasions, his regular partners, and some of his opponents, could tell that he was fuming, despite the bluff exterior. This should have been one of those occasions.

Dan was chagrined to realize that he himself had been so wrapped up in analyzing Clayton's failure to notice Doc's change of mind, and the resultant bottom, that he missed Clayton's lack of reaction to being fooled by the Doc.

The players who met after the game at the Cornerstone called themselves the Cornerstone Club. This was not an exclusive club— anybody who wanted to discuss bridge was welcome. Many of those who played in the Tuesday game would have liked go over the hands at the Cornerstone but seldom did. For players who were early risers, the club game by itself made for a late night and adding another hour plus a beer or two was too much. This was not the case for Katie Burton.

She lived four blocks from the Elks Hall and usually walked there and back on bridge nights. When she arrived at her door, after walking home from the game, she might briefly consider getting the car out of the garage and going down to the Cornerstone. Usually, the comfort of her favorite chair and a glass of sherry won that argument. If she had an idea for a Jay's Nest, the Cornerstone would not even cross her mind.

Katie continued to walk to the Elks Hall on bridge nights after Elsie died, despite not feeling as comfortable as before. Tonight she was almost home and walking lightly, because of her bridge triumph, when she heard footsteps behind her. She stopped and turned around. The only person in sight was big Russell Hicks. He waved as he turned into his mother's house. For the past few months he had been leaving his car in his mother's driveway and walking from there. This allowed him to check in on her before bridge and, if the lights were on, after the game as well.

Katie waved back and turned into her walk. She unlocked her front door and locked it again behind her. Locks didn't get much use in Pemberton. For many years, virtually everyone left their doors unlocked. Then there had been a flurry of minor burglaries. Long-unused keys, if they could be found, were put to use. Burglars seldom had much of a career in a small town. Sooner or later someone would sight them at a time and location that was out of place. Then, when it was discovered there has been a burglary, the suspect could be described, named and, if the officer was not a local, an address supplied. When the Bronson boys were apprehended, Pemberton's little crime wave came to an end, and folks gradually went back to leaving their doors unlocked.

Since Elsie's death, there had been a vague feeling of unease in Pemberton, mainly because there had never been a satisfactory explanation for why Elsie was running across the railroad bridge. This gave rise to rumors that somebody was spying on the Carmichaels and speculation that Elsie had been running from someone, or something, when she crossed the trestle. It had been nine months since Elsie's death, and Katie still got a little nervous when she was out alone at night.

The nervous feeling dissipated when Katie reached the safety of her home. She regained her sense of euphoria and poured a glass of sherry as a special reward. She started composing a tribute to Clayton in her head. She had fallen into an endplay from time to time, but this was a first — an expert play planned in advance that worked exactly as it was supposed to work. The only disappointment of the evening had been Clayton's lack of response when she told him about it. He congratulated her, but his heart didn't seem to be in it.

Perhaps he was still down, poor man, still mourning. Some people said he didn't always behave well at the table, but she had never seen that side of him. She had a soft spot for Clayton. When Katie's husband died, she went to see Clayton, a financial advisor, to set up annuities and to make investments. Clayton had done an excellent job and whenever they met after that he greeted her like a long lost friend.

The bridge club livened up when Clayton started courting Elsie. He was gregarious and outgoing, even as a beginner. When Elsie brought him to the club, he knew how to follow suit and not much more. Elsie was a life master, but she played with him in the novice section for a few weeks until he was comfortable with the mechanics of the game.

Clayton had an aptitude for bridge and it wasn't long before they had their first win. Of course it didn't hurt that Elsie was the second-best female player in Pemberton. Still, to give Clayton credit, he would have been a life master within a few years, were it not for Elsie's dog shows. She was off to a show almost every weekend and Clayton didn't like her go on her own.

Katie shook her head, took another sip of sherry, and got back to the problem at hand. The tribute to Clayton was going nowhere. It was unusual for her to have trouble with the main story line of a column. If the bidding or the play was technically difficult, she would get assistance from Fran. The table action, on the other hand, usually flowed from her pen. She seldom had to ask for help with that.

It was a strange coincidence that the subject of her column was Clayton Carmichael because the only column that had given her more grief, in four years of writing the Jay's Nest, was the tribute to Elsie Carmichael. That was months ago. Elsie had died on a Saturday. On the following Monday, Judd called Katie to say that the next issue of the *Chronicle* would be dedicated to Elsie and he wanted to know if she could feature Elsie in a Jay's Nest column. This was something Katie had never done. Elsie had no foibles and made none of the mistakes that led to entertaining bridge. She was steady and reliable: great as a partner, boring as the subject of a bridge column.

Fran had been Elsie's main partner before Elsie went off to Europe. After several false starts, Katie considered doing an interview with Fran about Elsie instead of a Jay's Nest column. She discussed this with Fran and they talked about what Fran might say.

Elsie's main virtue as a partner was that she was dependable. Elsie was not a skilled technician, but she always knew whether her seven of spades was good or whether the opponent who bid 1NT had already shown up with 14 HCP and therefore could not have the ace of diamonds. Elsie had a good memory for bidding agreements and she always had her bid. In short, said Fran, she was just a squeeze and an endplay short of being the ideal partner. In the mid-sixties, Fran and Elsie twice joined forces with two pairs from the Soo and both times got to the finals in the Canadian Women's Teams. Fran said that while most of the players in that event were more skilled than Elsie, there was nobody that Fran would have preferred as a bridge partner.

Katie thought this a very nice tribute to Elsie, but it was not a substitute for a Jay's Nest. Then, Katie remembered a column she had worked on for a while but had not finished. Katie had not been at the table when Elsie played the hand, which made writing about it much harder than she would have expected. On the plus side, she had kept her interview notes.

After several false starts, Katie had made it work by abandoning her own voice completely and turning the column over to Elsie. In the course of several interviews, Elsie had said everything two or three times. By artfully combining conversations, Katie was able to write a column that was 99% in Elsie's own words.

Now, almost nine months later, Katie wondered how it stood up.

Katie stored all her back issues of the *Chronicle* in the spare bedroom. She went in search of the memorial edition from the Friday after Elsie jumped off the trestle.

It took Katie a few minutes to find her copy of the *Chronicle* dated Friday, July 30, 1982. She turned immediately to the Jay's Nest. She scanned it quickly. *It's okay*, thought Katie. Elsie's voice gave it a different feel from her own columns. Nonetheless, it was clear she and Elsie had one thing in common. They were both much nicer in the flesh than when they were writing bridge columns.

Why Elsie had jumped was a mystery. Nine months had gone by and it was still a mystery. *It's too bad*, Katie mused, *that nobody saw what happened.*

C H A P T E R

In fact, many pairs of eyes watched Elsie jump. Trains crossed the bridge several times every day and Oak Canyon birds and animals went about their business with little more than an occasional glance. A running woman was another matter. This novel sight coupled with the squeal of air brakes got the full attention of squirrels, crows, blue jays, woodpeckers, two porcupines, a skunk, and a family of raccoons in a shallow cave with a panoramic view of the scene.

There were also three human observers, not counting the train engineer. None of them came forward at the time of the accident. Two of the witnesses were a couple who had reason to conceal their presence in the blueberry patch. The third witness started down the bank of the ravine, intending to help, but fell and twisted an ankle. The third observer did not see the couple (nor vice versa, though there was a brief moment when all three were on the edge of the ravine and were clearly visible to one another). Nursing the twisted ankle and watching the scene below, the third spectator was enveloped by a dark cloud — an awful feeling that the event was not entirely accidental and that Elsie's husband Clayton Carmichael was somehow involved. This feeling persisted, even though Clayton was not an actor in the scene and was, in fact, several miles away in Pemberton. Without paranormal insight, there must have been something tangible which led to the dreadful feeling. With a vision of Elsie plunging from the trestle, a vision that would last a lifetime, it was impossible to think of what the connection with Clayton might be.

THE PEMBERTON CHRONICLE

Friday, July 30, 1982

IN MEMORIAM

On July 24, Elsie Carmichael (nee Hamilton) plunged to her death from the railroad bridge over Oak Canyon. She is believed to have been picking blueberries on the west side of the ravine. The engineer reported that as soon as he had a full view of the trestle he spotted Elsie running towards him. He braked as much as safety allowed but with no hope of stopping in time. Elsie jumped and fell 45 feet onto the rocks of Oak Creek.

The bridge is designed for rail traffic only. There is no planking for a pedestrian walkway, no railings and no room to stand aside when a train comes through. There are warning signs on both sides of the bridge prohibiting foot traffic.

It is not known at the present time why Elsie was on the bridge.

Editor's note: Some of our regular features are being held over for a week to make this issue of the *Chronicle* a tribute to Elsie. In ad-

dition to a history of the Hamilton Brickworks and a brief biography of Elsie, there is an opinion piece on the remarkable popularity of bridge in Pemberton. First, an unusual Jay's Nest, by Elsie herself.

Note from Jay: "The Jay's Nest" bridge columns are based on deals in which I was involved, usually as declarer. This account is an exception. The deal featured in this column was played four months ago when Elsie was very much alive. I tried to write it up at the time, but the point of view was all wrong and I set it aside. When Judd asked me for a Jay's nest featuring Elsie, I looked at what I had done on this deal. After several more false starts, I realized it would be better if I wrote as though Elsie was speaking. Fortunately, I took a lot of notes from Elsie and Phil at the time and I have been able to use Elsie's own words almost exclusively. This is what I think she would have written.

The Jay's Nest

A guest column

by Elsie Carmichael

South dealer
E-W Vul.

```
           North (Phil)
           ♠ Q 5
           ♡ 10
           ♢ A 7 6 3
           ♣ A 10 9 7 5 2
West (Kit)              East (Clayton)
♠ 10 7 4               ♠ K 3
♡ Q 6 2               ♡ K J 9 8 4
♢ K J 10 4            ♢ Q 9 5
♣ K Q 6               ♣ J 8 3
           South (Elsie)
           ♠ A J 9 8 6 2
           ♡ A 7 5 3
           ♢ 8 2
           ♣ 4
```

I was the dealer and held an in-between hand — too weak in high cards to be opened one spade; unsuitable for a weak two-bid on several counts: four cards in the other major; an ace outside of the trump suit; the spade suit is not solid enough. When this deal was played at other tables, some Souths passed, some bid one spade, some bid two spades. I was the only player to find an opening bid of four spades.

This is not the way I usually bid. As much as I enjoyed the result, this leopard is not going to change her spots. It came about as the result of an alignment of stars and planets that is unlikely to occur any more often than a solar eclipse. Phil and I were

playing the second of two boards against my husband and my cousin. They got a top against us on the first board and the two of them were so smug I wanted to smack them. Instead, I decided to take a page out of Phil's playbook. I knew that Clayton and Kit would never anticipate my risqué four spade bid because I'm not that kind of girl. They didn't know that Phil has been encouraging me to loosen up my preempts at favorable vulnerability — this was why he didn't raise me to slam with his excellent support.

Phil is the only person with whom I could make this bid. Phil himself breaks every rule in the book. Once in a while this gets him accused of cheating, but breaking rules is not the same as breaking laws. Rules are not laws. Phil always plays within the law.

Rules are guidelines for smart players to follow. Some players break rules because they don't know any better. Phil is a free spirit. It makes him hard to play with and even harder to play against.

When I stepped out of character, I was thinking in terms of preventing Clayton and Kit from finding their best contract. The payoff came instead from their defense.

After the lead of the club king to dummy's ace, I had two options in the play. I could ruff two of my losing hearts. Then I would still have two red-suit losers, so I would have to try to bring in the trump suit for one loser. My second option, the one I chose, was to try to draw trumps for no losers and also hope that the clubs split. This, I thought, was less likely to succeed, but the payoff would be greater. I've never been a great technician — Phil later pointed out that this second line has a zero chance of success unless there was a serious mistake on defense. That is where my reputation came to my rescue.

Clayton usually defends well because he thinks ahead. As soon as Clayton saw the dummy, I knew he was thinking about what he would do when I played the spade queen from dummy. I never open four spades without two of the top three or three of the top five, so covering would do no good. Furthermore, he knew I had at least seven spades and probably eight, so even if I had stretched a little and was missing the spade ten, Kit would need to have three to the ten for covering to promote a trump trick. That, of course, was impossible.

In other words, his mistaken reasoning convinced him that covering would do no good, so he might as well pretend he didn't have the king. Maybe I would find a way to go wrong. What finally tipped the balance in favor of ducking was that he thought, 'What if Kit has the stiff ace?' That would mean I opened four spades with an eight-card suit: J-10-9-8-7-6-4-2. That was also impossible. However, as long as his play only mattered if I had made a bid that was completely out of character, the last thing he wanted to do was play his king and have it gobbled up by Kit's stiff ace. He would be hearing about that from Kit for the next year. He spent so much time thinking about whether covering might promote a trump trick that he didn't notice that covering would put me in the wrong hand for setting up the club suit.

When I played the spade queen from dummy, Clayton followed low without a care in the world. He was, if anything, too uninterested. I let the queen ride and it won, so I was still in dummy. Ruff a club. Ruff a heart. Ruff a club. Draw trumps. Back to the diamond ace. Pitch losers on the clubs. Take all the tricks! Yowza!

Thank you Elsie.
Jane Seabrook

* * * * *

The Pemberton Chronicle was a weekly. The special memorial issue was widely read, even by those for whom most of the information was common knowledge. Many read it to see what had been left out.

The day that this special edition of the *Chronicle* was published, the paper arrived at Jake Harden's farm gate just as he was walking from the barn to the house. Jake went past the house, out the lane to the road, collected the paper and then returned to the house for breakfast.

Jake would ultimately read every word of the paper, but his special interest was the history of the Pemberton area. He told his wife, Susan, and daughter, Jenny, that as a special treat he would read the history of the Brickworks to them over breakfast.

This was, of course, not a special treat. It was, however, part of a family tradition. Jake always ate his oatmeal porridge very fast, finishing well ahead of Susan and Jenny. Susan liked to say he inhaled it. Rather than leaving the table, Jake would read something out loud to the slow pokes while he drank his coffee.

"A History of the Hamilton Brickworks, by Greg Sanderson," began Jake.

"Who's he?" asked Jenny.

"How quickly we forget. He's Elsie's distant cousin, who stayed with them last summer and wrote a treatise on the history of the Brickworks, much more detailed than this, as part of his Master's program. He visited us one weekend and you thought he was handsome and charming."

Jenny blushed. "I did not."

Jake continued reading. "Pemberton is fifteen miles north of the St. Mary's River, a short broad channel with the remarkable distinction of connecting three Great Lakes: Superior, Michigan and Huron. The St. Mary's River was a meeting place for the ancestors of the Ojibway people a thousand years before Moses led his people out of Egypt." Jake paused for a sip of coffee.

"What has Moses got to do with the St. Mary's River?" asked Jenny. "Does this Greg Sanderson guy think the Ojibway are a lost tribe of Israel?"

"I think he just wants to emphasize that this area has been inhabited for a long time." Jake made a mental note to ask Jenny what she knew about the lost tribes and where she got her information.

"When Europeans discovered there was a continent on the other side of the world, the St. Mary's River became important for the fur trade and for travel, by explorers, settlers and the military, to the interior of North America. This was Ojibway country and while there were a lot of people passing through, there was very little settlement until copper was discovered near Bruce Mines in the 1840s. In 1850, a treaty was signed by the Ojibway to allow settlement in a huge tract of land, sometimes called The North Shore, which took in all of the potential agricultural land from Sudbury to Thunder Bay."

"What did the Ojibway get?" asked Jenny. "A few beads and blankets?"

"There were actually many separate treaties involving land rights, cash, and perpetual annuities. I'm sure advantage was taken by the treaty makers, but the Ojibway were much more sophisticated than the beads-and-blanket Indians from the time of Columbus.

"Ned Hamilton emigrated from Ireland in 1864. At the age of 23 he had eight years' experience as a brickmaker. When the government opened up the Carter River valley for settlement in 1866, offering land at twenty cents per acre, Ned was one of the first settlers to stake a claim, buying 160 acres for thirty-two dollars. Ned intended to be a farmer, but he noted that the clay in the bank of the Carter River was suitable, at several locations, for brickmaking and he chose one of those stretches of the river for his homestead. Should he ever decide to build a brick house, the raw materials would be at hand. A mile down the river from Ned, William Pemberton settled with a large family. His oldest daughter, Jenny, was seventeen and had many suitors, including Ned Hamilton. She enjoyed the attention but seemed in no hurry to choose a husband. Ned decided to build a brick house to help her make up her mind. "

"Who did you say wrote this?" drawled Susan. "It clearly wasn't a woman."

Susan had been so quiet that Jake assumed she was not listening. Apparently she was half listening, at a minimum. The question sounded rhetorical, so he continued without answering.

"When the house was complete, thirty-three year old Ned carried a nineteen-year-old bride across the threshold.

"The Hamilton family continued to farm, but brickmaking supplied them with most of their income. When Ned Hamilton turned the operation of the Brickworks over to his son Edward in 1909, the original Hamilton farm had long since been gutted to feed the brick factory. Ned became a farmer once more on 360 acres, three miles northeast of

Pemberton. He was a gentleman farmer this time, with hired hands to do the heavy labor."

"If you were a gentleman, would we have some hired hands?" said Susan.

"Daddy is always a gentleman," said Jenny.

"Yes he is."

Jake ignored them. He was accustomed to a certain amount of sniping. "Ned's new home, which became known as Hamilton House, was a solid two-and-a-half story brick house with one unusual feature. The south-east corner rounds into a tower which supports a turret that goes a full story above the roof and provides an excellent view of the Carter River Valley for miles in all directions."

"It's really cool," said Jenny. "The Carmichaels invited our grade eight class out there for a field trip. We went up to the top, five at a time. From the second floor you go into the tower and up a circular staircase and at the top you step out into the open air. It's kind of scary. Even though we were surrounded by a very solid curved brick wall that goes up to my shoulder, it's pretty high. The wall has slots that make the tower look like a giant chess piece from down below."

"The slots are called crenellations," said Jake.

"You have to remember, dear," said Susan, "that every child who grew up in the Carter Valley, including your mom and dad, went on a school field trip to Hamilton House. It's an experience you don't forget. Do they still have a little covered cupboard up on the turret with enough pairs of binoculars hanging in it for everybody to have a good look around the valley?"

"Yep, it was fantastic. But there were just five pairs of binoculars. That must be why they only allowed five of us to go up at a time."

Jake cleared his throat and picked up the paper again. "Edward got caught up in the optimism of the 1920s and embarked on a major expansion with plans to extend his market into Southern Ontario, Michigan and Illinois. The thirties caught him very much overextended and he survived only by cutting operations severely and selling the town house and all but ten acres of his father's farm. When Edward died suddenly in 1942 of a heart attack, his only son, William, inherited a failing factory with old equipment. William managed somehow to hold on for ten years, selling just enough bricks to pay the bills.

Several times during this period, the workers accepted shares in the company in lieu of part of their wages.

"When the brickworks began to prosper once more in the 1950s, William was still the major shareholder, with 35 percent of the shares, but Hamilton Brickworks was now a public company. When William died of a heart attack in 1969, the Brickworks was a thriving business once again.

"Dave Johnston, manager of the Brickworks, is the first non-Hamilton to become president of the Hamilton Brickworks. Nevertheless, Elsie Hamilton made certain that the accomplishments of Ned Hamilton will be remembered. In three years, in 1985, Hamilton House will become the Hamilton Brickworks Museum."

Jake frowned. "That's not accurate," he said. "As a member of the board of directors for the Hamilton Museum Foundation, I know it was incorporated in 1973 and ownership of the house was transferred to the foundation."

"And we are very proud of you, my dear," said Susan. "But didn't you yourself say that Hamilton House would not become a museum until 1985?"

"What I said was that it would become an *active* museum in 1985. In fact, it's been officially a museum since 1974, soon after Elsie got back from Europe. She expected to continue living there until the summer of 1985, sort of as a guest of the museum. When she got married, she and Clayton lived there, but it was understood that they would find another place to live by August 1, 1985."

"Weird," said Jenny.

"Not at all," said Jake. "It takes a lot of planning and collecting to get ready. In fact, Elsie and I had several discussions before she left for Ireland in 1970. She hired Mary Garson to housesit while she was away and there were two rooms of the house designated as museum storage rooms even though, at that time, the house was still in Elsie's name. She informed the Brickworks of her intentions and since then, worn-out tools and equipment that might have gone to the dump have been coming to Hamilton House. While she was in Ireland, she sent back several crates of artifacts that date from Ned Hamilton's time."

"I wonder," said Susan, "how Clayton felt about living in a museum when he and Elsie tied the knot?"

"I don't know how he felt at the time, but the day before yesterday, at the reading of the will, he seemed to feel that the museum was getting too much of Elsie's estate."

"Surely there's nothing he can do about it," said Susan.

"I don't know. Estate law is apparently very complicated. She didn't exactly cut him out of the will, but the spouse is guaranteed certain things."

"How much is he getting?" asked Jenny.

"Nobody knows yet. There'll be taxes and lawyer's fees and gifts, such as a new taxi for Kit, that come off the top. The executor is allowed up to a year to figure it all out. I'm sure it would be enough to make us feel rich."

* * * * *

While Jake's family was eating breakfast and being treated to *A History of the Hamilton Brickworks*, Kit McCrea, Elsie's first cousin and owner of Pemberton's only taxi, was driving Jim Campbell (the Professor) to the Soo Airport. Jim was responsible for the steam plant and the furnaces at the Brickworks. A brick plant in Oakville was going out of business and Jim was flying down to see if there was any equipment that the Brickworks ought to be bidding on. He would be staying overnight and couldn't drive himself to the airport and leave the car there (as he would have preferred) because his wife needed their car today.

Jim was called the Prof by most of Pemberton. When he was with Kit, he preferred to be called Jim. Whenever Kit called him 'Prof', (without any apparent ill intent) the name was infused with a hint of irony.

Once they were on their way, Jim took the *Chronicle* out of his briefcase. "I could read some of it to you, if there's anything you want to hear."

"I don't need to hear Elsie's bio one more time," said Kit. After a minute he yawned and said, "There's something in there about why Pemberton has so many bridge players. I glanced at it. Looks like a piece of crap. Why don't you read that? I feel like shooting fish in a barrel."

Jim started to read. "The Popularity of Bridge in Pemberton, by Greg Sanderson. The Pemberton Duplicate Bridge Club has almost as many members as clubs in towns that are ten times as large. I believe the reason can be found in the fact that Pemberton is on the North Shore."

"See," said Kit. "Right there. Cousin Greg has already gone off the rails."

"How so?"

"Along Highway 17, or within a few miles of the highway, between Sudbury and the Lakehead, there are twenty-odd small towns. Pemberton is the only one with a bridge club."

"The only one with a *duplicate* bridge club," corrected Jim. "Most of these towns have a bridge club or, at a minimum, a group of bridge players who get together of an evening for a few rubbers."

"But are there more bridge players than in towns of a similar size, say, along the old highway between Toronto and Montreal?" asked Kit. Jim didn't know the answer to that.

He continued, "One hundred years ago, in the evenings, people might go out occasionally to a concert or a play, but most of the time they entertained themselves. There were no phones, radios, televisions, movies. Roads were poor by today's standards and car tires were unreliable. Traveling for more than a mile or two was a project. The ways in which people entertained themselves were many and varied. Activities included book reading, singing, debating and game playing (both outdoors and indoors). Every house had a horseshoe pitch. The only houses without a deck of cards were the ones in which cards were prohibited because they could be used for gambling.

"Auction Bridge evolved into Contract Bridge in 1925. It became the dominant member of the Whist family of card games, and was soon the most popular of all card games.

"By 1925, the automobile was becoming reliable. There were more movies and most homes had a gramophone or radio or both. There was no shortage of entertaining ways to spend an evening."

"Okay, there's another thing," said Kit. "Contract bridge wasn't invented until technology started to compete for our spare time. The way Greg tells it, contract bridge arrived in time to participate in the demise of card games, rather than rising to the top of the heap."

Jim had an answer for that, but since he was close to the end of the article, he decided to finish before making his case.

"Nevertheless, people who had grown up thinking that an evening was not complete without a few hands of bridge continued to play. Some of their children would learn the game. Many would not. And their children's children were even less likely to play bridge.

"The difference for Pemberton and for many other small towns on the North Shore is that the Canadian Shield makes a formidable barrier of trees, rocks and swamps which isolates Northern Ontario from the rest of the world. Electricity, good roads, and television became readily available twenty to thirty years later in Northern Ontario than in Southern Ontario. This, in turn, meant that game-playing continued to be a widely chosen leisure-time activity in towns like Pemberton for about twenty years longer than in towns in the south."

"Basically," said Kit, "Greg is saying that bridge is popular in Pemberton because we are a bunch of hicks who are too ignorant to realize there are other things we could be doing with our spare time."

"Or maybe he is saying," countered Jim, "that given the isolation of the North Shore, the citizens of Pemberton had to rely on their own resources for entertainment and a surprising percent of them chose the most intellectually challenging of all social games."

Jim paused, but Kit was taking a minute to digest this, so Jim continued, "The other factor is that a significant technological advance has less effect on adults than on their children. Even if the adults took advantage of the new opportunities, they would continue to make time for their favorite activities, like playing bridge. The effect of each advance is not felt until the next generation."

"I'm always willing to admit when I'm wrong..." started Kit. Jim swallowed hard and kept his mouth shut. He didn't know anybody less likely to admit he was wrong than Kit. "...but this theory of Greg's still sounds like a crock to me. Nevertheless, I've got to say you sure know how to put a positive spin on it. That probably makes you a good teacher."

Jim's jaw dropped. Kit had never acknowledged that he was a good teacher.

"I should drop in on your classes sometime," offered Kit.

"Please don't," said Jim. "You'd frighten my students."

"You don't think I could help?" Kit was more puzzled than insulted.

"You're too good. The best players are seldom the best teachers. The most effective teacher once had the same problems as his students and still remembers how hard some things were."

* * * * *

At noon that same day, Dan joined Phil at noon at Mary's Lunch, as he did almost every weekday. They talked about many things, and most of all they talked about bridge. Today, Dan had an agenda. Even though he was retired, he had been consulted informally by young Grant Jones about Elsie's jump from the trestle. He wanted to find out if there was anything important to know about Elsie that hadn't been included in the *Chronicle* biography.

Dan was pleased to find that Phil, as requested, was looking at the article in the *Chronicle* when Dan arrived. "What I'd like to do," said Dan, "is scan the article while you eat your lunch. Whenever I come to something where I have a question, I'll get your comment. Meanwhile, you can make a note of anything you'd like to add or contradict."

"Okay," said Phil. "When you get to the tomboy reference, let me know."

Elsie Mary Hamilton Carmichael, (May 2, 1941–July 24, 1982). Elsie's mother, also called Elsie, died bringing her first child into the world. Raised by her father and a series of housekeepers, Elsie was burdened by a grandmotherly name from her mother and the expectations of her father. Elsie was his only hope of keeping the brickworks in the family and when his control of the shares dropped below 50%, that dream became a faint hope. Nevertheless, he encouraged her tomboy tendencies and steered her into a business program at the University of Toronto.

"What did you want to say about Elsie as a tomboy?" asked Dan.

"When we were kids, Franny and I used to go out there to swim. Beavers dammed up the creek so there was a good-size pond at the foot of the trestle. Elsie was two years older than us, a big difference in age when you're that young. We weren't buddies, but sometimes she'd come down and join us. The beaver dam added a couple of feet to a natural pool, making it deep enough for diving from the trestle. Franny never had any interest in jumping or diving, but Elsie was something of a tomboy, just like the paper says. Sometimes we'd work our way up the trestle for higher and higher jumps. She never showed me up, but she never let me beat her either."

"So Elsie had a foolhardy side," mused Dan.

"I wouldn't say that. She was brave, for a girl. Brave, period, for that matter. But she was also careful. She told me she did a survey of the pond from a little raft her dad made for her and she knew the exact water depth for the whole pond. Where there were boulders close to the surface, where it was deepest and safe for diving or jumping.

"When I look back on it now," continued Phil, "and picture us diving off the trestle, there's one little part of the picture that didn't register with me until very recently. I was always the one to go a little bit higher and she always equaled me. She was never the one to challenge me to go higher. I was almost a teenager and full of myself, so I assumed she was keeping up with me because she didn't want to be shown up by a kid two years younger than her. When I picture us up on that trestle, I was the one that was nervous as we went higher, not Elsie. In fact, in my imagination, she's so damn comfortable I'll bet she routinely went higher when there was nobody around to push her to new heights."

"If I have this right," said Dan, "you only just realized she held back because she didn't want to embarrass you and didn't want to push you to a height that might have been dangerous for you."

Phil grunted wordlessly and went back to his coffee. After a moment lost in thought, Dan turned his eye back to the biography.

Elsie worked at the Brickworks every summer from the time she started high school. On graduation from the University of Toronto, she became department head of Purchasing and Raw Materials. She was responsible for seeing that everything necessary to make a brick was at hand when the brick was ready to be made. Under her were competent responsible workers who knew their jobs, so her department pretty much ran itself. If there was resentment that a young woman had parachuted in to be their boss, they kept it to themselves. It helped that when there were decisions to be made, she consulted them and made responsible decisions. Meanwhile, she had lots of time to garden and play bridge.

"You would have been working at the Brickworks the same time as Elsie," said Dan. "What did the other employees think of her?"

Phil shrugged. "She'd been doing odd jobs at the Brickworks every summer for close to ten years, so everybody knew her. We became good friends. She wasn't a snob and didn't throw her weight around. The other workers liked her, but they didn't take her seriously. Women's lib has been slow to reach Pemberton and even slower to reach the floor of the Brickworks. They knew what her father had planned for her, but they would have laid odds that she'd get married and have babies before the time came for her to be the manager."

Dan nodded, and found his place again.

William was confident that Elsie had what it took to be a good manager. He intended to gradually increase her responsibilities over the next ten years so that when he was ready to step down, she would be the natural person to take over his position.

William didn't know that he had inherited his father's heart. He died when Elsie had been on the job for four years.

Elsie loved her father and would have done anything for him. She doubted the board would make her president of the Brickworks as her father wanted. She was too young, too inexperienced, and too female. The Brickworks acting manager was good at his job and well liked. Nevertheless, out of respect for her father, she campaigned for the position. The shareholders voted. She lost by a narrow margin.

Elsie had always wanted to travel. She sold most of her interest in the Brickworks and retained Hamilton House, three miles northeast of Pemberton. She resigned her position at the Brickworks and spent the next three years in Europe, going first to Ireland where she visited several brickworks including the one where Ned Hamilton did his apprenticeship, which was still in operation.

When she returned to Pemberton in 1973, she met several times with a lawyer in Bruce Mines to create the Hamilton Brickworks Museum Foundation and to transfer ownership of Hamilton House to the foundation. She was at loose ends as she left his office. There was another office in the same building with a sign on the door that read Clayton Carmichael Financial Consultant. She knocked on the door and went in.

"Why would she consult Clayton?" asked Dan. "She had a business degree from the University of Toronto. She was probably better qualified to make financial decisions than Clayton."

"She was always careful and thorough," said Phil. "She would have wanted to be sure she hadn't overlooked anything."

* * * * *

Mid-afternoon of that same Friday, a week after Elsie's death, Fran walked into Mary's Lunch to pick up a blueberry pie. Mary made her own pies. Whole pies were available by special order. Fran's pie was in the oven and would be out in five minutes. The only patron in the restaurant was Christine, who was reading the Jay's Nest column in the special edition. Fran strode over to Christine's table and asked, "Can I join you for a few minutes?"

"Please do," said Christine, putting the paper down, leaving it open to Elsie's post-mortem Jay's Nest. "I don't usually eat at this time of day, but I'm doing a series of paintings of the sun setting over Lake Superior. A nice young man at the Agawa souvenir store offered to let me know whenever the weather and cloud conditions promised spectacular sunsets. I just got a call. From supper time to dusk, if the lake and the sky and the sun cooperate, I'll be a very busy painter."

"The sunsets are magnificent up there," Fran agreed. "In fact, at the bridge club on Tuesday, I noticed you still have a bit of a limp from the last time you were up there."

Christine glanced down at her ankle and then explained. "That was from a hike through the bush to a rocky part of the shore that gave me a great view of the lake. I intend to go back there, but not until my ankle's a hundred percent. For now, I'll be satisfied with the view from the beach at Agawa."

"Do you do sketches first, or will you try to complete a painting on the spot?"

"Sketches. But I do some pigment mixing and try to get the colors right."

Fran looked around. There were two reproductions on the walls of the restaurant. One was an old barn, the other an anonymous lake. "Have you any completed paintings that haven't been shipped to Toronto?"

"A few. And I have a few more that are almost finished."

"Maybe you should ask Mary's son Eddie if you could hang some of them here. Put prices on them and offer Eddie a small commission on any that sold."

"Do you think Eddie would be interested?"

"Interested in what?" asked Eddie. The seductive smell of a hot homemade pie filled the air. Eddie placed a cardboard box on the table next to Fran. "Keep it level until it cools."

"Christine is a painter," said Fran.

"That I know. Does she need a model?" asked Eddie.

"I think she needs a piece of pie," said Christine.

"She needs a gallery," said Fran. "You have two walls in here that would be almost classy if they had some original oils on them. I take it back. This place will never be classy, but oil paintings would make it more interesting."

Eddie seemed disappointed that he wasn't going to become a model, but he told Christine to bring in some of her paintings any weekday between two and three in the afternoon. He promised he would get his mother to come out of the kitchen to have a look and they would make a decision."

"Blueberry?" asked Eddie.

"Definitely."

Eddie returned to the kitchen and Fran started to get up.

"Before you go," said Christine, "can I ask you a question about Elsie?" She held up the paper. "I didn't know her very well, but the person who supposedly wrote this Jay's column doesn't sound the least bit like Elsie to me, especially the 'Yowza.' Did Elsie really say that or is Jay using artistic license?"

"Elsie said it, but not at the table. That was later, when she and Phil were telling Jay about the deal. Elsie was a competitor. She was also kind and considerate — which would be the Elsie you were used to meeting at the bridge table. You have to remember, though, that she was groomed to be the king of the castle, not the queen. She was definitely less refined than you might expect from the lady of the manor. The 'Yowza' was typical of the Elsie I knew. The four-spade bid is what you should be looking at. It was completely out of character. She never made gambling bids, no matter what the situation. A couple of gloaters could not have provoked her enough to make her step that far out of character."

"So the smugness of her opponents was not what provoked her?"

"Exactly," said Fran. There was something in the way she said it that implied Fran knew what had provoked Elsie.

"Please tell me!" Christine said, with an urgency that caught Fran off guard.

"Will you promise to keep it under your hat?"

Christine promised.

"What I'm about to tell you may not be true. That is, I know what I heard, but I may have drawn wrong conclusions. First, you have to know that Elsie's reluctance to go to tournaments with Clayton had nothing to do with her dog shows. As Clayton got better at bridge, it became apparent that he was both a poor loser and a poor winner. When he lost, he looked for ways to blame his partner and when he won, he took the credit. That much you can take to the bank. Jay may not have known this, but it's general knowledge among the few of us who go to tournaments with him."

"Why do you play with him, then?"

"Clayton's bad form was worst with Elsie. He's more restrained with the rest of us. Also, when he's at his best, he's an entertaining guy and a pretty good bridge player." Fran started to get up again.

"Wait! What was it that made Elsie take a flyer?"

Fran sat down again. "I played with Dan that night and we started against Phil and Elsie. When we were chatting before the game, Elsie said Clayton wanted to hire a professional to be his partner at the upcoming Nationals. She also said that they had no money for that sort of extravagance. Undoubtedly, Clayton felt they did. I got the impression that they had a heated argument about it, but that's just an impression."

"If there's any suspicion of foul play in Elsie's death, that might be considered motive," said Christine.

"Yes, it might. That's why you can't repeat what I just told you. It'd lead to a miscarriage of justice. Clayton might be capable of wishing Elsie would fall off a cliff, but he doesn't have it in him to push her over the edge."

* * * * *

Corey Garson, born and raised in Pemberton, was relatively new to bridge. She got married while still a teenager, and now had three children, the youngest of whom, Angie, was still at home when Corey was made a widow by a snowmobile accident. Corey took bridge lessons from the Prof and had been a bridge club regular for two years. She and Angie had just finished supper and Angie had gone out to do homework with a classmate. Corey was reading the *Chronicle*'s tribute to Elsie when her sister Mary knocked and walked in.

Corey had known Elsie from bridge. Mary had a different connection — she shared a grade with Elsie when they were in school and they'd become friendly but not friends. Mary started cleaning at Hamilton House when Elsie was working at the Brickworks, and they gradually became close. When Elsie went to Europe, she recruited Mary to housesit. After Clayton and Elsie got married, Mary cleaned for them once a week. Two days ago, Mary had been invited to the reading of Elsie's will. She would receive an indexed annuity that paid twice her current wage. In the words of the will: "This monthly payment will more than cover her wages if Mary chooses to continue to do regular cleaning but is not contingent on that — Mary is to receive the payment regardless."

"Hello Sister Mary," said Corey. Mary was definitely not a Sister in the Catholic sense of the term. Their grandmother had been a gypsy and when Mary got divorced after two years of marriage, she had moved in with Granny, looking after her until she died at the age of 87.

"Do you know what I find odd about this bio of Elsie?" said Corey. "It stops when Elsie meets Clayton as though it was understood that they lived happily ever after."

"Maybe," said Mary, "they're following the principle that if you can't say anything good, don't say anything at all."

"I thought they were happy."

"I think they were happy for at least a year. Then some cracks started to show."

"Such as?"

"Little things. They never argued in front of me, but sometimes there was more silence than usual. Or excessive politeness when they did speak."

"It'd be more remarkable if they didn't have occasional disagreements," said Corey.

"You asked."

"Okay. I guess it would depend on what they were arguing about before the silent treatment."

"There were hints. One time Elsie dug out a blouse that she bought in France years ago. A simple blouse with some exquisite floral embroidery. She gave it to me for no reason at all and I had a silly smile plastered across my face for most of the day. Elsie said that when I smiled like that, I was an amazing beauty. She said it was a wonder I didn't have every single man in Pemberton lined up outside my door. I said looks will get you a roll in the hay, but for attracting a man for something longer term, I preferred a nice inheritance. That's when she got this look on her face. She said the trouble with an inheritance is you don't know whether he's looking at you or your bank book. She didn't say more and I didn't pursue it."

Corey frowned, but didn't say anything.

"Another time out of the blue she said that the nicest man in Pemberton was Phil Stinson. And he's available. Has been for years. I suggested he's gay. She said no, he's just waiting for a nice lady to propose. She said that's something she didn't realize when she was young or she might have married him instead of Clayton."

CHAPTER

The morning after doing a pseudo endplay (with malice aforethought), Katherine Jane Burton, nee Seabrook, awoke wondering why she felt so chipper. Then she remembered. Her big house, large and empty since her husband's death, seemed bright and airy this morning. After breakfast she returned to her column. She looked at what she had written the previous evening and it still didn't feel right. After worrying at it for another half hour, she set it aside until noon when she could call Fran, who taught at Pemberton High. At twenty past noon, Fran would have had time to get home and finish lunch.

When the phone rang, Fran picked up with, "Hello, Katie."

"How did you know it was me?"

"It's a quarter past twelve, it's Wednesday, your column is due at four o'clock. Of course it's you."

Fran should have been a detective. Katie launched into her problem.

"Your dummy is king third, stiff jack, king queen fourth..." After many such calls, Fran had trained Katie always to give the complete deal before the problem, starting with the North hand and to give the suits in order of rank, naming the honors and giving the length of each suit. Like most experienced duplicate players of above-average ability, Fran had in her mind an empty mental template of a bridge deal, into which she slotted the cards as fast as Katie could say them. In order for this to work efficiently, the cards always had to be given in the same order, spades, hearts, diamonds, clubs. At the end of this exercise, Fran's mental picture would resemble the deal as it would appear in a bridge column.

This time, Katie's description was unnecessary. "I know the one," said Fran. "You executed a pseudo endplay."

"Yes, I did," said Katie. "I've never had such a thrill. It wasn't just that it was an expert play. It was that I did it, as Dan would say, with malice aforethought. Sometimes I fall into an expert play. I've even done a squeeze, but I didn't know it until you told me later. Planning an expert play and then doing it is a whole different ball of wax. It was better than sex, not that sex was ever that great." Fran made an amused noise over the phone. "The only fly in the ointment is that the column doesn't sound right and I can't figure out how to fix it."

"Okay, let's hear what you've got."

Katie started to read. "This column is dedicated to Clayton Carmichael who invented the pseudo endplay and generously explains it to anyone interested in improving their play. The purpose of the..."

"Stop, stop, stop," said Fran. "Clayton didn't invent that play, but that's not the problem. This is completely out of character."

"I'm usually nice and I like to give credit," said Katie.

"You're not usually nice — you're always nice. But Jane Seabrook isn't. You've developed a persona as Jane, the author of The Jay's Nest, and the fact that Jane likes the nickname Jay is part and parcel of a personality that is quite unlike the personality of Katie Burton. Jane Seabrook doesn't start columns with that sort of pompous twaddle. And she doesn't blow her own horn as I'll bet you were about to do. In Jay's Nest columns, someone is always playing the goat rather than Jay playing the hero."

Katie felt her cheeks grow warm and stared fixedly at the article in front of her.

"Put it aside," continued Fran. "Leave it for a few weeks until the glow wears off. Then maybe you'll be able to write about it. For now, you better submit one of your reserve columns."

"I don't know if I have anything," objected Katie.

"Of course you do. You could use the one about Mac that we talked through last week. And there are several others we've hashed over that I haven't seen in print."

"I guess."

"Leave it for now. But you should talk to the Doc about that deal. He might give you a way in."

"What do you mean?"

"Gotta go. See you next Tuesday. Good luck." Fran could be aggravating, but Katie could never have done these columns without her.

* * * * *

For her part, Fran was delighted with the Jay's Nest columns, both because they were fun, and because they revealed a side of Katie she'd known and loved as a young girl and which she'd thought was gone forever. When Fran got off the phone, she made a cup of tea, went into the den, and sat in a rocking chair in front of the picture window with a panoramic view of the Carter River. Noon was usually a hectic time with a husband and three teenagers home for lunch. Today, all four of them had a noon-hour activity. Fran had twenty-five minutes in which to sip tea and watch the river flow by.

Until she was twelve, she and Katie, Debbie Carter and Terry Seabrook had been the four musketeers. The summer of 1948 was their last and best as musketeers. They went camping together, picked blueberries, played softball, and bicycled to Bruce Mines several times. The adventure of the summer had been a bicycle trip through the back roads to Echo Bay followed by a ride on the milk-run freight train for the return trip.

Years later, Fran had fond memories of the train ride, but recalled best the adventure of the twenty mile trip from Pemberton to Echo Bay.

The bike ride to Echo Bay, much of it on two-track gravel roads, took most of the day. All of the country roads were gravel in those days. Even a freshly graded gravel road quickly developed pairs of smooth tracks from the repeated passage of pairs of wheels along the same course. There were some long hills that they rode down at breakneck speed over loose gravel. It was a miracle they completed the trip without any crashes. They stayed the night with relatives. Next morning came the treat Fran had been negotiating with her uncle since the previous winter. He was a brakeman on the CPR and arranged for them to hop the freight, putting their bicycles in an empty boxcar. They rode in the engine as far as Bar River and during the stop, while empty milk cans were being unloaded, they went back to the caboose, where they rode for the rest of the trip.

Everything looked different from the train, including villages like Isbester and Portlock, which were little more than a station and a few houses. (They disappeared completely once Highway 17 was paved and trucks started hauling milk and farm supplies.) The train stopped at Bruce Station and they bicycled home from there.

That summer was the last for the musketeers. Over the winter, they all grew up a little. By the next summer, they each had responsibilities that cut into their free time. Fran supposed they all went through some changes as they became adults, but for no one was the transition as abrupt and complete as it was for Katie. In the space of a few months, Katie lost twenty points of IQ, most of her athletic ability, all of her musketeer's aggressiveness and independence, and she learned the art of looking up in wonder at boys who were shorter than herself. In short, she never again threatened a male ego.

Fran checked the time. She had twenty minutes to get back to school. Pemberton High was on the other side of town. Close enough that she could have walked, far enough that she seldom did. As she drove, she wondered whether she had been too abrupt with Katie, but decided no. Despite her soft exterior, Katie was a tough bird.

The Jay's Nest columns had first come to Fran's attention when Dan Cogan got in touch with her about a release from the bridge club. Judd Harris down at the *Chronicle* had frequent contact with Dan while he was on the force. He knew that Dan played at the bridge club, so when Katie went to Judd with some sample articles, he called Dan. Judd thought the articles would make good copy for the paper and good advertising for the bridge club, but he didn't want to get a lot of letters from bridge players who felt they were being pilloried.

Fran liked the sample columns — they were not great bridge but they were amusing. Nevertheless, she understood why Judd wanted a release. The columns had much more of an edge than one would have expected from Katie. As the president of the club, Fran announced on several successive bridge nights that Katie Burton would be writing a weekly column. Fran emphasized how good it would be for the club without bothering to mention that she had sample articles in hand. She explained that since individual players would be named, the *Chronicle* wanted explicit permission from every bridge player in the club before they would go ahead with the columns. No one had high expectations, but everyone knew Katie wouldn't hurt a fly, so Fran had no difficulty getting the signatures.

When the column began appearing in the *Chronicle*, Pemberton discovered there was a side to Katie they had not suspected. Because the articles were fundamentally good-natured, no one was sufficiently upset to complain to the paper. Kit McCrea made frequent appearances in the column, always as an expert but seldom as a successful expert. Kit had mixed feelings about this. When he asked Katie if she thought she was being fair, she replied, "Oh Kit, that's just show business. I exaggerate to make it more interesting. You don't mind do you?" Kit did mind. He wouldn't have broached the subject otherwise. But he wasn't about to admit he minded, so Katie carried on.

The column usually appeared on the editorial page. There was a time when Judd had a lot to say and would not have tolerated being squeezed by a bridge column. That time was past. Judd had expressed most of his opinions many times over and he was happy to surrender some of his editorial space. Some of Katie's columns were quite long, but Judd rarely complained.

The columns were popular, and not just among bridge players. Everybody knew Katie and could scarcely believe that she was writing the columns. They kept reading them to see what she would say next. The different person that came through in the columns shouldn't have been a complete surprise to Fran, because Katie was different as a bridge player than she was in everyday life. More assertive for starters. Katie was barely average as a player, but she scored better than it seemed she should because she bid aggressively and took full advantage of sloppy play.

Fran drove into the teachers' parking lot with ten minutes to spare and sat for a minute as she thought about Katie's bridge personality. Fran wondered if it owed something to her personality from the musketeer days. Young Katie had been athletic, mischievous, bright and somewhat absent-minded. It was a personality she shed without any apparent regret. She became a correspondent, writing lengthy letters to friends and relatives who went on extended holidays or had moved away from Pemberton. Fran had seen a few of these letters, enough to note that Katie's writing reflected her new personality without any hint of resentment or rebellion. Her best correspondent was her cousin

Terry, former musketeer, who went to be a nurse in Kingston and married a teacher there. It was Terry, the first recipient of a Jay's Nest column, who urged Katie to take some samples to the *Chronicle*.

After Katie married and the children were in school, Katie's letters started to change. A glimmer of caustic wit appeared, which became more pervasive until it colored everything she wrote. This was a change that Fran didn't learn about until after the emergence of the Jay's Nest columns. The curious thing about this change in Katie's style was that it was confined to her writing. It never found its way into everyday life.

When the Jay's Nest appeared in the *Chronicle*, Fran thought the exposure would trigger a change in Katie. It didn't happen. Katie had two separate personalities which seemed to be aware of each other, but were neither embarrassed nor affected by the other personality. The closest Jay came to emerging from the page was during discussions with Fran about the Jay's Nest. At such times, Katie expressed views and made comments she would never have made at other times. Katie was able to maintain this separation because she regarded Jay not as another personality but as a fictional person she had created. She had used her middle and maiden names as a semi-pseudonym to emphasize that the views and criticisms of Jay were in no way connected with her own. Fran, on reflection, viewed the Katie of the past thirty-five years as a fiction and Jane Seabrook as the real Katie.

Fran looked at her watch. Fifteen minutes had gone by. She was now five minutes late. She opened the car door and made a dash for her classroom. As she neared the door, she could hear the vice-principal on the PA system making the afternoon announcements. She slowed down, composed herself, and strolled into the classroom just as the announcements were coming to an end.

C H A P T E R

Pemberton was Dan Cogan's adopted hometown. In 1950, Dan and Connie came north from Stratford in what Dan thought would be a smart career move — more responsibility, more variety. They planned to stay for five years. Thirty-three years later he was still here. The same could not be said of Connie.

When Dan arrived in Pemberton, he had a wife and a baby girl. Life was good for Connie and Dan, and it got better. A year later, the old Seabrook place came up for sale. The big frame house was sound but neither quaint nor luxurious. There was lots of room for Dan, Connie, a two-year-old girl and a baby boy. The large house was a bonus. It was the lot that sold them (sold Connie, truth be known). Nearly two acres with a small barn that had been converted into a garage and tool shed. There was an orchard, raspberries, and a large vegetable garden. They would never have been able to afford such a place in Stratford.

Connie and Dan were very happy in Pemberton as five years stretched into ten. Dan had a responsible job that he liked doing and he did it well. Connie had a larger garden than she had ever dreamed of. They had two healthy children and they had each other. It felt to Dan as though their move to Pemberton was a move to the Garden of Eden. He scarcely noticed that spring came a month later than he was used to and fall came a month sooner. Connie noticed, of course, because it had a direct bearing on her favorite hobby. At first, she was determined not to make an issue of it.

In the beginning, Connie did all of the garden planning and most of the planting, weeding, watering and harvesting. Dan was sometimes allowed to use a shovel or push a wheelbarrow. Connie's grandmother had a large garden, Connie's mother a small one. Connie had grown up loving both. Dan had no gardens in his background. His father was a steam engine mechanic, his mother a clerk, and they lived in an apartment in downtown Stratford where the only plants were geraniums and African violets.

In those early years, Connie had the vegetable garden plowed every year. In fact, for a few years, plowing was something to write home about because it was done by old Lester Gordon with a team of horses and a single furrow plow. Lester said horse plowing was the only way to turn over a garden — those newfangled tractors packed down the soil too much. Dan thought two one-ton horses versus one two-ton tractor was pretty much a wash, but it pleased Connie to have her garden plowed by old Lester, so he kept his opinion to himself.

In the winter of their fourth year in Pemberton, Lester had a mild heart attack. The doctor told him his days of wrestling with a horse-drawn plow were over. That spring, Lester's son Jimmy came by with his Fordson tractor and two furrow plow and did in fifteen minutes what it had taken his dad more than an hour to do. Jimmy, however, had a farm to look after and wasn't always available when Connie was ready to plant her peas. Several times over the next few years, Dan did the spring plowing with a shovel. Turning over the whole garden took a few hours a day for a week or more. Then Connie did some landscaping, which left no room for a tractor to turn at the end of the garden and turning over the soil with a shovel became a regular spring chore. Dan didn't mind. He liked physical work and he found that once he got into the rhythm, his mind could go off somewhere else and leave his body to do the shoveling.

The vegetable garden gradually became Dan's garden. The transition started with the corn. Though Connie loved having a kitchen garden large enough to grow everything, she found that many vegetables were less reliable in Pemberton than they had been in Stratford. Tomatoes were often just starting to ripen when the first frost came. Vine crops didn't always make it. Sweet corn was usually a success, but was borderline if the summer was cool.

Corn on the cob was a special treat and the corn from their kitchen garden was superb. Fifteen years after they arrived in Pemberton (by which time Connie knew that the plan to go back down south was on permanent hold), the summer started wet and cool and then turned hot and dry. In late August, the corn was late and doing poorly. It looked as though they would get just a fraction of their usual harvest. Two days before the first cobs would have been ripe, raccoons made a night raid and destroyed the corn patch.

"That's it," said Connie, "I'm finished with corn. If you want corn you'll have to grow it yourself."

Since corn was Dan's favorite garden crop (Connie knew this, of course), he accepted the challenge. He tackled the corn problem in very much the same way he would later tackle the game of bridge. His first step was to research corn in Connie's library of garden books and magazines. He discovered, to his surprise, that Connie's library was not as comprehensive as it had seemed. Most of her books were survey books and their treatment of corn was superficial. The same was the case for the magazine articles — occasional tidbits of information ladled up with great dollops of cheerleading. He realized that Connie, with her rich garden background, read books and magazines for inspiration and for an occasional hint at something new to try. She didn't need or want a comprehensive treatise. Come spring, Dan had worked his way through all of Connie's back issues of *Organic Gardening and Farming* and talked to a local farmer who grew sweet corn. He was confident he could grow a pretty good crop of corn. He was determined to do well, though he had a hunch that if he had a bumper crop, Connie might not be entirely pleased.

He needn't have worried. For a few years, his corn crops were adequate but no threat to Connie's status as the master gardener. As he was more thorough than Connie in his research, he probably knew more about corn than Connie, but acquiring a gardening touch came slowly.

When Dan was starting to feel pretty comfortable with corn, Connie had a green bean crop failure (blight) and Dan found himself in charge of them as well. Next came the vine crops (late spring frost) and then the tomatoes (cool summer, no ripe tomatoes).

There were two crops, peas and potatoes, which clearly grew better in Pemberton than in Stratford. The final straw came when the peas, which were in bloom and promising to be abundant, suddenly wilted en masse — they just curled up and died. The neighbor, Johnny Bates, had sprayed his lawn with weed killer and enough had drifted

fence to kill Connie's ultra-sensitive peas. Dan might not
 .ade the connection, but Johnny had killed his own peas as well.
 .and Johnny came to an understanding about how Johnny would
treat his lawn in the future, but it was too late to placate Connie. She
handed over the peas and threw in the potatoes for good measure. She
continued to tend the flowerbeds, but the vegetable garden became
Dan's.

When Connie's mother needed homecare a few years after Dan
took over the peas and potatoes, Connie went south and didn't come
back. The kids had already gone off to school and would not be re-
turning to Pemberton. For the last few years before she left, he and
Connie were little more than familiar strangers. Though they had been
drifting apart, her departure left an empty space in Dan's life.

He seldom felt that empty space in the morning. He had always
been the first to rise, making his own breakfast — milk and brown
sugar on hot shredded wheat biscuits (made by pouring boiling water
over the shredded wheat and then draining). Then coffee. His morning routine was unchanged. There was always reading material on
the table. At present it was mainly back issues of *Bridge World*. While
playing at a club game in the Soo, Dan discovered a notice on their
bulletin board for a set of *Bridge World* magazines which was almost
complete. The price was $300 for 604 old magazines. The fact that
none of the Soo players snapped it up meant they must have thought
the price steep. For Dan, it was a bargain. All of the ideas in bridge for
the past fifty years had appeared in the pages of *Bridge World*. It was
the bridge expert's magazine and even if Dan did not expect to become
a bridge expert, he still wanted to play in their game.

After breakfast, on the morning that Katie was struggling to make
her triumphant pseudo endplay into a Jay's Nest, Dan spent a little
time on a bridge puzzle and then went out to dig at the top end of his
garden. It was drying nicely and would be okay for peas in another
few days. In the first few minutes of digging, Dan concentrated on
what he was doing, pushing in the shovel every six inches, noting the
moisture content and friability of the soil. The subsoil was heavy clay
but the garden topsoil was dark and easy to work. The garden had
been in pretty good shape when they arrived and additions of sand and
organic matter had completed the transformation of heavy clay into a

dark crumbly topsoil which broke up as each shovelful was half turned and dropped back in place. He would plant the peas soon, probably on Sunday.

Continuing to dig, Dan turned to a double-dummy bridge problem in which he was supposedly able to make five notrump. He worked on it after breakfast without getting anywhere.

When he started to play duplicate, he had trouble remembering the cards in the last trick. Now, after an evening in which he played twenty-six boards followed by a discussion at the Cornerstone, he was able to remember the main details of all twenty-six deals. In the case of the double-dummy problem, he had studied the hands in this deal for several hours over the past few days and he knew every spot.

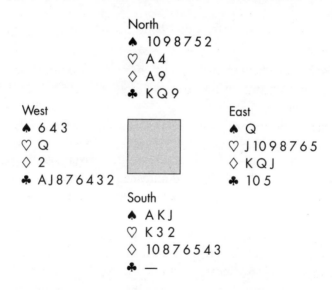

North
♠ 10 9 8 7 5 2
♡ A 4
♢ A 9
♣ K Q 9

West
♠ 6 4 3
♡ Q
♢ 2
♣ A J 8 7 6 4 3 2

East
♠ Q
♡ J 10 9 8 7 6 5
♢ K Q J
♣ 10 5

South
♠ A K J
♡ K 3 2
♢ 10 8 7 6 5 4 3
♣ —

After the lead of the queen of hearts, South has to make five notrump. This was a double-dummy problem that Kit got from somewhere. Kit didn't have a solution, but Fran had worked on it and solved it (so she said) in twenty minutes. Dan thought he had it solved after just a few minutes, but on further study realized the defense could prevail against his line. The thing about double-dummy problems was that in return for seeing all four hands, you had to assume the defense was perfect.

The term "double-dummy" puzzled Dan when he first heard it. Why call it double-dummy when you were shown all the hands? He soon realized that that was the point. When there was a single dummy, half of the cards were known (the dummy plus your own hand). But with two dummies, three hands would be visible and the one remaining concealed hand could be deduced. So the location of all the cards was known.

It was interesting, this dummy business. In trick-taking card games with no dummy, play and defense were pretty much a random thing with a minimum of planning and strategy. With one dummy, enough became known about the closed hands to allow considerable planning and strategy, both by declarer and by the defenders. It was the dummy which set bridge apart and put it head and shoulders above other trick-taking games like Hearts, Euchre, and even Whist, the granddaddy of bridge.

Two dummies, on the other hand, reduced bridge to little more than a chess endgame with cards. Gone were deception and percentage plays. Gone were signaling by defenders and remembering that your eight of spades was good. Gone were table presence and deducing holdings from the bidding.

Victor Mollo's Hideous Hog likes to say, "I always play double-dummy." And, of course, to bid and play as though you could see all the cards was the goal of every serious bridge player. But if it were ever achieved, the game would be diminished. As far as Dan could see, there was no danger of that happening. Nevertheless, it was a tribute to the complexity of the game that even when all the cards were known, there were hands on which the best line of play was very hard to find.

In the play of this particular deal, he needed eleven tricks: he had six spade tricks, two hearts and one diamond for nine tricks. If he played the club king, it would lose to the ace but dummy's club queen would then be Trick 10. It looked as though he would have to squeeze East in the red suits for Trick 11.

The thought of squeezing East sent Dan off on another tangent. The concept of a squeeze was simple enough. When a defender guards two suits and has to make a discard that unguards one of the suits, that defender is being squeezed. Defenders don't have to be good players to sense they are being squeezed. On the other hand, executing a squeeze as declarer can be very difficult. It was generally considered to be an expert play and Dan had struggled with squeeze play technique. The fact that Dan could think, somewhat casually, of squeezing East meant that he must be making progress with the most common squeeze situations, at least. There were many types of squeezes including some exotic ones which would be recognized at the table by no more than a handful of bridge players worldwide. Dan did not expect to join their ranks.

Back to the double-dummy problem. On the run of the spades, East would have to make five discards. This was the position Dan kept coming to (with the lead in the North hand); he needed three of the last five tricks:

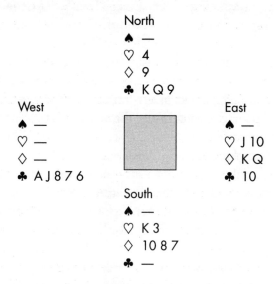

North
♠ —
♡ 4
◇ 9
♣ K Q 9

West
♠ —
♡ —
◇ —
♣ A J 8 7 6

East
♠ —
♡ J 10
◇ K Q
♣ 10

South
♠ —
♡ K 3
◇ 10 8 7
♣ —

If North plays the club king and West wins with the club ace, West is endplayed and must return a club, which gives North two club tricks on the finesse. As North cashes the clubs, East has to pitch two red cards, which allows South to win the last two tricks on the squeeze. Making twelve tricks (one more than necessary). So, of course, West won't play the club ace on the play of the club king and now North has a club trick but must lose three of the next four tricks. One trick short.

After working at the double-dummy problem for a while without finding a way around this impasse, Dan moved on to the Clayton problem — different than the bridge problem but just as puzzling. Clayton Carmichael had been an acquaintance for years. Soon after Dan took up duplicate, Clayton asked Dan for a game. Clayton was also a recent convert to the game — anyone who has been playing serious bridge for less than ten years is a recent convert. Clayton was somewhat better than Dan at the time. Dan felt he was now the stronger player, but they continued to play regularly. They didn't spend much time together away from the table but had developed a comfortable bridge-playing friendship.

Their friendship had not been quite as comfortable since Elsie's death. Something elusive in Clayton's behavior kept nagging at Dan. As soon as he started to think about it, the uneasy feeling disappeared. The incident from the previous night brought him back to it once again.

Clayton was the sort of man who carried himself with an air of satisfaction. When Clayton encountered an obstacle, he tended to get annoyed. He was pragmatic and usually found a way to set things right in his world. Elsie's death had set him back, but he recovered quickly and got on with his life. In fact, if anything, his life seemed to get better for a while. Then, in recent months, he became less cocky than was customary for Clayton Carmichael, and at the bridge table he seemed to have lost a little of his competitive edge.

Dan had a detailed account of the circumstances surrounding Elsie's death because Jonesy was the investigating officer. Young Grant Jones had been on the force for twelve years. In the last two years before Dan's retirement, Jonesy worked with Dan whenever there was an investigation.

After Elsie took her plunge, Jonesy came by to get Dan's take — it looked like an accident but suicide was not out of the question. There was also the possibility that Elsie was chased, though they found no evidence of it. While they were at it, they considered Clayton. When a woman dies, you look at the husband (no matter what the circumstances) until it is clear the husband had nothing to do with his wife's death. So when Elsie died, it was natural that Dan should wonder whether Clayton could have been responsible. Elsie's inheritance was big enough to be a motive. That aside, Jonesy had nothing and Dan was unable to come up with any reason for suspecting his friend. Furthermore, nothing new had come to light in the nine months since Elsie had died. The chance of finding out what happened that day was pretty remote. Dan was becoming resigned to this mystery remaining a mystery. He would discuss it with Phil at noon and if nothing more came of that conversation, he would put it to bed and try to forget it.

Between the digging and daydreaming, Dan was still in his garden when the noon whistle went off at the Brickworks. He was going to be late for lunch. By the time Dan arrived, the daily special was being placed in front of Phil. The food was plain at Mary's, but soup and pies were made on the premises each day and were always very good.

The decor was simple and unassuming — plywood paneling below window level, white painted walls above the paneling. For many years there had been two paintings on the walls, one of a decaying barn, the other of a northern lake. These had been replaced with paintings done by Christine Williams, the artist from down south. When Christine decided to remain in Pemberton over the winter, she arranged to hang paintings here and at the Cornerstone. Not that she would sell anything, with prices between $350 and $800, not when you could get perfectly good pictures from Woolworths for under $100. Then again, a cottager from up north of Rock Lake had come in for coffee and said the prices were quite reasonable and he would be back with his wife when they came up for the summer.

Most of the paintings were realistic without any attempt at photo-realism. Kit, who claimed to know a little about art, said it was obvious Christine's main influences were the Group of Seven and the French Impressionists. There were five paintings. The largest was different than the others. It was an abstract — a gray-black line went from side to side with green lines dropping down and meeting at the bottom to form an inverted triangle. In the middle of the triangle was a stroke of blue. Dan found this painting neither beautiful nor interesting. It was surprising that it was not fading into the background. Dan ordered soup, coffee and a piece of pumpkin pie, and then asked Phil, "Have you ever wondered whether Clayton had a hand in Elsie's leap off that trestle?"

"Doesn't seem it could be anything but an accident," responded Phil without pause. Dan did a double take. Phil seldom gave an immediate answer. He must have already considered the question. Dan waited for a few seconds for him to amplify, but Phil had said his piece.

"I've been through it from every angle," said Dan, "and Clayton comes out clean. But there is something off about the way the man is acting. Take last night when he was swindled by the Doc. Or maybe I should say when Doc declined to be swindled. Clayton was a little put out, but there was no righteous indignation at a miscarriage of justice. I suppose even nine months after Elsie's death we should expect him to step out of character once in a while, but it doesn't feel right — this is not the Clayton we know and love."

"He's got a perfect alibi," said Phil. Another quick response. It was clear that Phil had been giving the matter some thought and probably could have said more.

"Exactly. It's too good — nobody ever has that good an alibi — and how come we knew about it when nobody was even asking for an alibi? It just happens that at 4:34, just minutes after Elsie jumped off that trestle, Clayton was buying a book on the care of your dog at Garner's where they have that new cash register that prints out the date and time of purchase on your receipt. I even tried driving from Garner's out to the Hamilton place, but in five minutes I didn't even get to the railroad crossing and it's another long mile to the house."

"What did he do with the dogs?"

Dan looked at Phil for some indication of where that question had come from, because it was one of the things that didn't feel quite right. "Damn it, Phil! For a guy who thinks Clayton is innocent, that's a very pregnant question."

Phil just shrugged and Dan continued, "Clayton said he sold the dogs because they reminded him of Elsie, but he did it right after her death when he should have still been in shock. In other words, when he shouldn't even have realized yet that the dogs were going to remind him of her. Clayton, after all, was something of a dog man himself."

"I have another question but I'm afraid to ask in case it's too pregnant."

"Take a chance."

"Anything ever come of the theory she was being chased?"

"Nothing. They wondered right away if she might have been running from a bear. Bears are very fond of blueberries. Next day they got Trapper Johnson from over Wharnecliffe way to come and look for signs. He found some bear scat but he didn't think it was recent enough."

"A bear," said Phil, "is the only thing I've been able to come up with that is half way likely. Anyone, like Elsie, who picks a lot of blueberries, has run into a bear or two in the blueberry patch. But there're some problems with the bear theory."

"Yes, I know," said Dan, "The engineer saw no bears, and Trapper Johnson found no recent scat."

"That's not the problem," said Phil. "When the engineer saw a woman charging the train, he wouldn't be gazing about looking for bears. And when the bear heard a screaming train, it might not stick around to see what the fuss was all about."

"What about Trapper Johnson?"

"I have no doubt that if Johnson found scat, he'd be able to estimate how old it was, but can he guarantee he found every bit of scat there was to be found? Then there's the possibility there was a bear who didn't leave a calling card — maybe the bear was just passing through and didn't have time to stop for a shit. Or maybe the bear was constipated and was feeling a little cross and Elsie spotted it right away and took off."

"Okay, a bear is still a possibility," said Dan. "Then why do you have a problem with the bear theory?"

"For starters, Elsie was the bravest woman I ever knew. She wouldn't panic if she saw a bear. She was also sensible. If she saw a cub, she would get the hell out of there before mama showed up, but she wouldn't run. She would also have known that the train was due — it would take something very unusual to put her up on the trestle at train time."

"Jonesy said she wasn't wearing a watch. Maybe she didn't realize it was train time."

"She seldom wore a watch, but she once told me she could hear a train twenty minutes away by putting her ear to the rail. Even just laying a hand on the rail you can feel a slight vibration five to ten minutes before the train arrives."

"Maybe it wasn't a bear," said Dan. "There's rumors somebody was spying on them."

"It would have to be somebody pretty scary to make Elsie run. She'd be more likely to tell him to mind his own business."

"Right," said Dan. "Clayton said they sometimes noticed movement across the ravine, or a flash of light, like a reflection off a spy glass, but didn't think much of it at the time. Thing is, that's Crown Land over there — nothing but rocks, moss and scrub bush — and blueberries. It's an unofficial park for Pemberton. There's footpaths all over the place. In other words, there would be people over there from time to time and they probably weren't spies."

Phil had drained his coffee cup, shifted in his chair, fiddled with the salt, then the pepper, shifted in his chair, fiddled with the pepper, then the salt. Dan was lighting up when he realized what was wrong with this picture.

"You quit," Dan said.

"Maybe," said Phil.

"How long?"

"Twelve hours."

"Why maybe?"

"Well, I quit twice before. Didn't make it either time," said Phil.

"How long?"

"Three days the first time. Six weeks the second. Thought I had it licked that time."

"Maybe you should use the Professor's method."

"You mean smoke a pipe?" said Phil.

"No, he quit both cigarettes and the pipe."

"When?"

"Eight years ago."

"Maybe you know a different Professor. I've seen Jim Campbell smoking his pipe many times over the past eight years and I'm pretty sure I've seen him smoking cigarettes too."

"Guess he never told you about his method," said Dan. "Got kidded and shut up about it. But he's still on the program."

"So what you're saying is the Prof's got a way of quitting smoking where he gets to keep on smoking. Maybe I'm already on his program and don't know it."

"Maybe you are. The Prof's theory is that nobody ever quits the first time they try. They remember the good things about smoking and start to wondering, after a few days, if they're really serious about never in their whole life smoking another cigarette. Sooner or later they realize that they are going to have to try it again to see if it's really as good as they remember. If the time has been short, then they take up where they left off. If they've quit long enough to get clear of the physical addiction, they find they can have that trial cigarette without any problem. So a few weeks later they have another."

"I know the type," said Phil. "They smoke other people's cigarettes until they lose all their friends. Then they start buying their own again."

"Right. The Professor read back in 1974 that it takes about four months for a quitting smoker's lungs to go from gray to pink. So he decided to quit smoking for six months out of the year to give his lungs a chance to rejuvenate. Once he had done it and started again he decided to smoke one month less each year until he was down to one month a year and then to keep on that way for as long as he felt like it. He found that quitting got easier every year and he was looking forward less and less to starting again. The year before last he skipped his smoking month entirely and last summer he just smoked for two weeks."

"So once he was quit, why in the world would he start again?" He normally thought of Jim Campbell as a pretty sensible guy, but it seemed to Phil that the Professor was starting to sound like a nutcase.

"It's a deal he made with himself. It was easier to quit because he knew it wasn't going to be forever. And when he started again, it felt like a reward instead of a failure."

"I dunno. Maybe I'll go on the Professor's program and then just not start again."

"Then you wouldn't be on the program. If you've got the idea in the back of your mind that the quitting is permanent, then it won't work. You'd still have that thought about giving up a good thing for the rest of your life nagging at you and you'd still feel like a failure when you started again, so you wouldn't stop again on schedule."

"If you think it's so great," said Phil, "why aren't you on the program?"

"I didn't say I was convinced. I'm just presenting the case. Still it's true I think the Prof might be on to something. But first you have to want to quit. I like smoking."

Phil got up to return to work. Maybe the main advantage of the Professor's smoking theory was that in the discussion with Dan he had forgotten for a few minutes how much he wanted a cigarette.

Dan said, "Just a sec. Can you come for supper tonight?"

"Yep."

"6:30?"

"Yep."

C H A P T E R

As much as Dan liked Phil and especially liked talking bridge with him, there were times when Dan got impatient. Phil was typically a man of few words, except for when he was hot on the heels of a new theory. Then he would talk your leg off, but not until he had the new theory pretty much nailed down. In the early stages, he would say little or nothing at all. During their noon-hour discussion of Clayton, it was clear that Phil was holding back.

That evening, Dan avoided any mention of Elsie until they had eaten. After supper, Dan served the coffee and then reached into his breast pocket for a cigarette. He remembered and grabbed his pen instead. He congratulated himself on his smooth move and said "I'm making a list for Jonesy. I'd like to add the points that you avoided telling me today at Mary's."

"I guess I owe you something for not lighting that cigarette," said Phil. "I do have a couple of points, but they won't help you. If I had anything of any interest, I would've told you already. These points are just some random thoughts that don't lead anywhere."

"I'm just trying to make some sense of this. If we get enough random thoughts that lead nowhere, then sooner or later there'll be something that shines a light on some of the others."

"I have my doubts about any light being found here," said Phil. "Anyway, it's about whether or not she was being chased. The difficulty with that theory is that it would have taken a very unusual threat to spook Elsie to run across the trestle without first checking whether a train was coming. What should be considered is whether she was pulled rather than pushed."

"Not so cryptic please."

"Thing is, it would be very difficult to scare Elsie onto that trestle, to push her in other words; but it's easy to imagine something happening at the house on the other side of the ravine that made it urgent that she get there as quickly as possible—that would pull her across. Not many people would run across that railroad bridge at any time of the day, let alone when a train was due, just to save a pet. But Elsie would."

Phil continued, "My other point has to do with Elsie charging the train. Assuming she wasn't suicidal, which I think isn't even remotely possible, why didn't she hear the train sooner? Why didn't she turn around and go back as far as she could before having to jump? The bank of that ravine is steep, but she could have gotten close enough to cut the vertical drop in half. Finally, why didn't she stop and climb down into the support structure of the trestle?"

"I think I can answer the last one," said Dan. "I went out there with Jonesy and we considered that possibility. The supports under the rail platform are recessed just far enough from the edge that it would take an acrobat or an orangutan to swing out over the edge and then back underneath to grab the support structure."

"How about the second one?" asked Phil. There was something in the way he posed the question that suggested he had an answer himself

"Why not turn around? I have no idea. What do you think?" said Dan.

"When you run on railroad beds, you have to adjust your stride to the spacing of the ties — that often means adopting a short choppy stride. Also you have to concentrate on your lead foot — if it doesn't come down square on the tie, you can twist an ankle. That means head down, watching the ties and making fine adjustments to your stride. The train was probably visible for a few critical seconds before she glanced up and saw it. By then, there was no turning back."

Dan had to concede that Phil's observations were interesting but not useful. Dan was ready to close the book on this one.

CHAPTER 8

A week later at noon, Fran came in to Mary's where Phil and Dan were eating lunch. She sat down beside Phil.

"We need to talk about your mother," she said.

"My mother, eh?" Phil knew when their mother became his mother, something was up.

"She wants to go up to the Soo tonight and I've got volleyball practice with the senior girls."

"Can't it wait until the weekend?"

"Apparently not."

Phil knew better than to ask the purpose of the trip. Their mother was very secretive, even about matters as simple as a trip to the grocery store.

"Okay," said Phil.

There was a minute of silence. The mother discussion seemed to be concluded. Dan never failed to be impressed at how quickly the twins came to an agreement.

"I'm still working on that double-dummy problem," said Dan.

"Do you want a hint?" asked Fran. Then, before he could say no, she said, "It involves an endplay."

"That's where I am. But if West ducks the club king, there's no endplay."

Fran gave him a little half smile that he sometimes found very annoying and said, "Got to get back to school. See you next week." It would not have bothered him that the best player in Pemberton was a woman if she didn't have that little smile.

After Fran left, Dan thought briefly about the double-dummy problem. Even if an endplay is involved, some sort of squeeze is also necessary. "I'm getting comfortable with basic squeeze-play technique," said Dan, "but I'm still having trouble transferring theory to the table. I thought I had a squeeze Tuesday night, but it turned out my extra trick was just a pseudo."

"Don't bad-mouth the pseudo squeeze," said Phil. "A genuine squeeze is a brute force play — there's nothing the defender can do. With a pseudo, the defender has a safe discard which doesn't seem safe and a dangerous discard which seems less dangerous than the safe discard. Anybody with a bit of card sense can learn to execute a genuine squeeze, but it takes an artist to do a pseudo squeeze."

"What's so artistic about taking advantage of a mistake?"

"If your defender has a clear picture of the deal and still makes a mistake, it's not all that satisfying. But if you paint a false picture and sell it to a good defender, then you can claim to be an artist. Not all art is great art — the simplest deception when painting a false picture is to discard from the suit in which you hope to take the extra trick."

Phil took out a pen and wrote on a paper napkin:

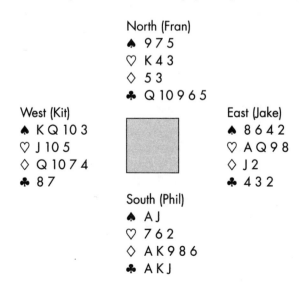

North (Fran)
♠ 9 7 5
♡ K 4 3
◇ 5 3
♣ Q 10 9 6 5

West (Kit)
♠ K Q 10 3
♡ J 10 5
◇ Q 10 7 4
♣ 8 7

East (Jake)
♠ 8 6 4 2
♡ A Q 9 8
◇ J 2
♣ 4 3 2

South (Phil)
♠ A J
♡ 7 6 2
◇ A K 9 8 6
♣ A K J

"The bidding is simple: Two notrump by me, three notrump by Fran. Kit leads the spade king and I win because I don't want a heart switch. I have eight tricks in top cards and might get a ninth if the heart ace is on side. As you can see, the heart ace is over the king and I have no legitimate play for my contract. Kit doesn't know this, however, and on the run of the clubs, Kit has to make three discards.

"Kit doesn't know who has the ace and queen of hearts, but if they are split between me and Jake, then Kit should keep all his hearts. He would like to keep all of his spades and diamonds as well, but can afford to discard one of each without giving up too much. I reel off five club tricks. On the third club, Kit discards a diamond. On the fourth club, I pitch the diamond six from my hand. Kit discards the three of spades.

"On the fifth club, I throw another diamond, pretending to have no hope for the diamond suit. Kit thinks for a while, but eventually buys it and discards a second diamond. I play three rounds of diamonds for my contract."

Phil put his pen down on the table with a satisfied thump.

He concluded, "There's other ways to paint a false picture to set up a pseudo squeeze, but discarding from the suit in which you hope to take an extra trick is effective and you don't need special skills to do it. Of course you sometimes deceive your partner as well and you have to put up with a comment that it is too bad you pitched those diamonds — you could have made two overtricks."

"Which gives you a chance to explain how well you played," said Dan.

"Not me. I apologize for my careless play. There's a better chance my victim will buy another painting."

"Kit won't believe you were careless," said Dan. "And he'll remember."

"Right. For Kit I would have to take that into account. Suppose, while this hand is still fresh in his mind, another hand is dealt where the West and North hands are identical to this one. The difference is that I have ace-fifth of hearts and king-third of diamonds. This would be the deal:

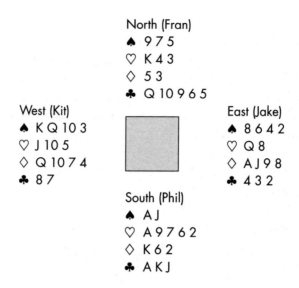

North (Fran)
♠ 9 7 5
♡ K 4 3
◇ 5 3
♣ Q 10 9 6 5

West (Kit)
♠ K Q 10 3
♡ J 10 5
◇ Q 10 7 4
♣ 8 7

East (Jake)
♠ 8 6 4 2
♡ Q 8
◇ A J 9 8
♣ 4 3 2

South (Phil)
♠ A J
♡ A 9 7 6 2
◇ K 6 2
♣ A K J

"The normal deceptive play would be to pitch a couple of hearts, but against Kit I pitch two small diamonds, same as the last time — Kit says, 'Not again,' and discards a heart, allowing me to win five heart tricks."

"Diabolical. But why wouldn't he discard a second spade instead of the heart?"

"That would leave his spade queen stiff. There's too many holdings where I could give up a trick to the spade queen and then make my contract with good spade spots."

"What about Jake's discards? Won't his signals spoil your painting?"

"Sometimes. And probably should in this case. The odd thing is that many defenders pay more attention to what declarer is doing than to their own partner. Also, sometimes a high spot, meant as a come on, is ambiguous because most of the low spots are visible or have been played."

Their coffee came and Dan reached for his cigarettes and then remembered that Phil had quit.

"You still off the weed?"

"I'm on the Professor's program," said Phil.

"Really on it, or just pretending you're on it until you get over the hump?" asked Dan.

"Really on it," said Phil, "but this is just between you and me."

"Okay, but what made you decide to try it?"

"I went into the lunchroom this morning for a coffee, after everybody had their break, and there were Shorty's Pall Malls lying on the table. I've been taking late breaks to miss the smokers but I wasn't even thinking about cigarettes when I went in there. I picked up the pack and turned it over in my hand. Just sort of studied it."

"So you had a cigarette," said Dan.

"Almost. I've been smoking filters for years now, but back when I really enjoyed smoking, I smoked Pall Malls. I looked at Shorty's Pall Malls and I thought 'this is ridiculous.'"

"A sensible person might assume you meant it was ridiculous to be holding a pack of cigarettes in your hand when you quit a week ago."

"They might," said Phil.

"But you were thinking it was ridiculous to be giving up something you enjoyed so much," said Dan. "What stopped you?"

"Steam."

"Steam?"

"There was a big whooshing hiss of a steam release from the boiler room. The Prof must have been shutting something down. It reminded me of his theory. I decided if I was going to smoke again anyway, I might as well give the Prof's method a shot."

"You immediately lost your craving for a smoke?"

"Don't I wish! The first few days after quitting are always the worst and I still don't go ten minutes without thinking about lighting up. But to give the Prof some credit, as soon as I decided to go on his program, even though I still wanted to light up in the worst way, the temptation was easier to resist. In other words, my addiction center is still sending out very strong messages urging me to smoke, but my brain is not crossing the line and siding with the enemy."

"The Professor's going to be really pleased to hear about this."

"No, he isn't," said Phil. "You're not going to tell him."

"It's got to come out sometime," said Dan. "Or when you start again, are you just going to let everybody think you just couldn't give it up?"

"Wouldn't be far from the truth," said Phil. "I'll cross that bridge when I get to it."

When Dan got back home, he sat down at the kitchen table and pulled out the double-dummy problem.

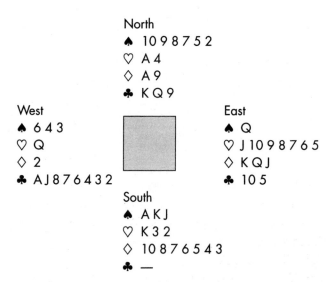

North
♠ 10 9 8 7 5 2
♡ A 4
◇ A 9
♣ K Q 9

West
♠ 6 4 3
♡ Q
◇ 2
♣ A J 8 7 6 4 3 2

East
♠ Q
♡ J 10 9 8 7 6 5
◇ K Q J
♣ 10 5

South
♠ A K J
♡ K 3 2
◇ 10 8 7 6 5 4 3
♣ —

He couldn't see any way to endplay East. With all those hearts, East can always play hearts without giving anything up. And West can avoid the endplay (as well as the squeeze) by refusing to win the first club; after that, North can't continue clubs without allowing West to run the rest of the suit. Dan continued to study the diagram. He tried many things, crossing off played cards as he went and then, every so often, making a new diagram. Several diagrams later, he saw the solution. And because he had been through the deal many times, he could see immediately how it would work.

He would win the first trick with the heart ace in the North hand, draw just two rounds of spades (playing the five and seven of spades from the North hand) and then cross over to the diamond ace. The key here is that West still has one more spade and that spade must be larger than the two of spades, the lowest card in the suit, which is still in the dummy.

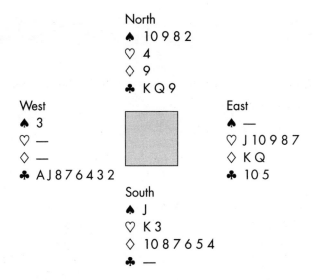

Now lead the club king, discarding the spade jack from the South hand, unblocking the spade suit. If West wins the club, then South will be able to win (in the dummy) whatever West plays next and squeeze East for eleven tricks.

What if West ducks?

On the club king, South pitches the spade jack and West lets the club king win. Now comes a most unusual endplay. North plays the carefully preserved spade deuce. This loses a trick in spades which doesn't have to be lost. But it comes right back because West is end-played. After he wins that trick, he only has clubs left, which means North will get a second club trick as well as an entry to dummy to cash the rest of the spades. It doesn't matter whether West cashes the club ace first or not. South will be able to squeeze East for the requisite eleven tricks.

Very pretty, indeed. The next time he saw Fran, he asked if it was true she had solved the problem in twenty minutes.

"Might have been less than that," she replied, "but it was the second time I solved it. The first time was ten years ago and I don't know how long I took that time. It's from a book called *Bridge Magic*."

This time her little smile was much less irritating.

CHAPTER

THE PEMBERTON CHRONICLE

Friday, May 6, 1983

THE JAY'S NEST
by Jane Seabrook

Dealer: North
E-W Vul.

North (Gary)
- ♠ J 5 2
- ♡ A Q 9 6 3
- ◇ 8 3
- ♣ 9 6 3

West (Peter)
- ♠ 8
- ♡ J 10 8 7 2
- ◇ A J 10 6 5 4
- ♣ 10

East (Rose)
- ♠ Q 10 9 7
- ♡ K 4
- ◇ Q
- ♣ K J 8 7 5 4

South (Jay)
- ♠ A K 6 4 3
- ♡ 5
- ◇ K 9 7 2
- ♣ A Q 2

West	North	East	South
	pass	pass	1♠
2♠	3♠	pass	4♠
all pass			

Opening lead: ◇A

After I opened one spade and Peter Duchesne overcalled two spades showing hearts and a minor, my partner should have been licking his lips in anticipation of the vulnerable penalty. But Gary bids his own hand and leaves the opponents to bid theirs. He doesn't like to be pushed around. When I opened one spade, Gary decided he had a spade raise and he bid it. Peter led the diamond ace, dropping Rose's queen, and continued with the diamond jack. I was expecting Rose to ruff. Who wouldn't?

When she pitched a club, it stopped me dead in my tracks. If anyone were going to duck, it would have been Rose, which is why we call her The Duck. She's a good player, so she can usually come up with a reason, even if it's one that doesn't wash with Kit. On this occasion, she was playing with her husband, who doesn't talk as good a game, so she had a little more latitude and would be able to win the post-mortem.

It finally dawned on me that she must have a natural trump trick. As much as Rose likes to duck, she's not in the habit of giving tricks away, so she must have figured that ruffing wouldn't gain a trick. If that was the case, then it couldn't cost me to give her a trump trick. So I won with my king and played another diamond. When Peter didn't cover, I let it run. Rose let it hold, discarding another club. I could see that this was going to be harder than I thought. Maybe she thought if she won the trick, she'd be endplayed. I played my last diamond, ruffing low in dummy just to tempt her, and still she pitched a club. So I played a spade and when Rose put in the ten, I let it hold! Two could play this game. She played the queen right back and I won that as Peter showed out, which told me I still had another trump loser. I shot back a little one to Rose's nine and she played another to my ace.

North (Gary)
♠ —
♡ A Q 9
♢ —
♣ 9 6

West (Peter)
♠ —
♡ J 10 8 7
♢ —
♣ 10

East (Rose)
♠ —
♡ K 4
♢ —
♣ K J 7

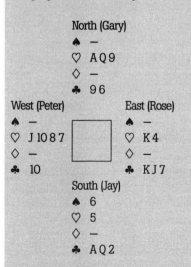

South (Jay)
♠ 6
♡ 5
♢ —
♣ A Q 2

This game of give-away was making me giddy. I slapped down my last spade, but of course Rose didn't have any more, so I had to win. Rose pitched a heart this time and I

stopped to take stock. I had lost all I could afford to lose and still needed two finesses to make my contract.

Peter had shown hearts and a minor in the bidding. Since he had shown up with six diamonds, that left Rose with most of the clubs, so the club finesse was probably going to work. The heart finesse should work too, since Peter's bid showed at least five, which would leave Rose with just two hearts to begin with. But Rose's heart discard had me worried. With any normal player, the heart discard would mean they had nothing to protect in hearts. Not Rose. Indeed, Rose's weakness is that she is predictable in her unpredictability — if she has two small, she keeps them both to make you think she is protecting something, but with king-small she pitches the small one to make you think she has nothing.

I was worried about the heart finesse, especially since, if it lost, I had no way to get back to the dummy to cash the ace. I love finesses, but I'm not quite so enthusiastic when losing the finesse means losing two tricks instead of just one. Besides, Rose had thrown so many clubs that maybe my club deuce would grow up. I played to the heart ace and, wouldn't you know it, Rose dropped the king.

Rose didn't win the post-mortem after all. When she's playing with an expert, she can talk about squeezes and such, but with Peter that doesn't wash. He and I both knew the heart discard was just a foolish attempt to swindle me.

C H A P T E R

When the Professor started giving bridge lessons, they were always held on a Monday night at 7:30. This was a convenient time for him and the Elks Hall was always available on Monday nights. As he became known as Pemberton's bridge teacher, he got inquiries about other times. Mondays were impossible for some, evenings for others. He tried other times and other days. If the Elks Hall was unavailable. he seldom had any trouble finding an alternate location.

In the spring of 1983, he was trying Friday at 5:00 to 6:30 p.m. for the first time. The location was the basement meeting room of the United Church Hall on River Street. The class was small. On the plus side, some of the students were first-timers because no other time had ever been convenient for them.

The class was billed as advanced. As usual, he did brief reviews of beginning and intermediate concepts for those who didn't realize how little they knew. There were two students in this class who were truly ready for advanced concepts. They were Corey Loucks, widowed mother of three, and Christine Williams, the artist from down south.

Christine was new to Pemberton. In her mid-twenties, lanky and athletic, she was attractive without being glamorous. Christine had come north the previous summer for the obligatory northern painting trip and stayed longer than she planned. She rented a small apartment in the Cornerstone and was frequently down in the bar on Tuesday nights when the bridge players gathered there after the weekly duplicate game. Christine started playing in the novice section on Tuesday nights and caught on quickly. She and Corey established a partnership and agreed to play on the first and third Tuesdays of every month.

Corey Loucks was a serious woman with a brilliant smile. The smile was seldom seen at the bridge club, not because she was unhappy, but because Corey was determined to improve her game. When she played bridge, she gave it her full attention. Progress had been slow, but it seemed to her she had recently reached a new plateau. The Professor's lessons, at any rate, were making much more sense this time around — she was taking the advanced class for the second time.

Applying what she learned was easier this time because of the partnership with Christine. They were close in ability and since they were taking the Professor's classes together, they almost always agreed about what they did or what they should have done.

Corey had started from home in time to pick up Christine and get to the church hall with a few minutes to spare. They usually drove separately, but today, after the lesson, they were going out for supper together. As they drove down along the river through the old part of town, Corey pointed out a large new house.

"Where that house now stands," said Corey, "there used to be a much smaller, less attractive house where I was born and raised."

"Nice location."

"I guess it depends on your point of view. I got married at seventeen, partly for love, partly to escape."

As they passed the Jackson house, Corey slowed down and pointed. "That house looks much the same as it did in my day."

"I've never been partial to insulbrick," said Christine.

"There was a time when I thought it was pretty nice," said Corey. "But times change. This used to be the poor part of town."

Corey braked to a stop behind two cars and a backhoe. The town was upgrading the sewer and water lines. The left side of the street was dug up and the backhoe was lowering a large pipe into the open hole on the right.

"There's no way to go around," said Corey.

"That's okay," said Christine. "If we're late, we're late." They were silent for a minute. "You said you escaped...?" Christine left it for Corey to finish the question.

"I may have given the wrong impression. We were poor, but we never went hungry. We had a big garden. My dad hunted and fished. We seldom had steak. Sometimes there was no meat at all, but there were always potatoes and some kind of vegetable and there was always dessert — either pie or berry preserves. My favorite memories from childhood were the family expeditions to pick strawberries, raspberries and blueberries. We were allowed to sell half of what we picked. It was the only time Mary and I ever had spending money. The rest was preserved. By fall, our basement was lined with rows of berry preserves."

Christine smiled lopsidedly. "If I'd known you then, I think I'd have been envious. I'd have loved those family excursions."

Corey glanced over at her. "You didn't have family outings?"

"I was an only child of a single parent. My step-father was nice, but he was a very busy man in a big city, so there was definitely no family berry picking."

"It could have been worse. When you went to school, were you dressed in yesterday's fashions? Were you left off the invitation list to a birthday party because of where you lived?"

"I would have hated that as a child," admitted Christine. "But, as an adult, the berry picking excursions would make for much richer memories than the birthday parties."

The backhoe got out of the way and waiting cars were allowed to pass.

The class was in progress as Christine and Corey entered. The Professor was reviewing safety plays. "Spades are trumps and dummy has three to the king," said the Professor, writing K-5-4 on the blackboard as the latecomers took their seats.

"Your spades are A-10-7-6-3." He wrote this underneath the K-5-4. "You will almost always have a trump loser with this holding and if the five outstanding spades split four-one then you may have two losers. How do you play to maximize your chances of holding the trump losers to just one trick?"

This had been the last example from the week before. "Cross over to the king and then finesse the ten on the way back," said Christine, just as Corey was about to volunteer the same answer.

"That's right. Once you play the king, you have to lose two trumps if the player on your left started with Q-J-x-x. But you can guard against Q-J-x-x on your right by finessing the ten. Of course the ten will lose to the queen or jack most of the time, but when that happens there will be just one trump outstanding and you can draw it with your ace.

"With some safety plays, you deliberately lose a trick that might not have to be lost in order to insure that you do not have two or more losers in that suit. In this case, you don't have to give up a trick in order to play safe. You just have to give up the losing trick on the second rather than the third round of that suit. By choosing to lose that trick on the second round, you guard against the loss of two tricks in the event that the player on your right started with Q-J-x-x."

As the Professor concluded his mini-lecture, Corey raised her hand and asked, "Do all of the good players know that play?"

This sounded like a trick question to the Professor, so he covered his bases as best he could. "Yes, they know it, but sometimes there are other considerations — if there were a danger in losing the trick to his left-hand opponent, declarer might just win with the ace and hope the trumps split three-two."

"Well, last Tuesday, a chance for that safety play came up at the table, only it wasn't me could've made the safety play. Dan Cogan got to four hearts and I had Q-J-x-x, so I was waiting for him to do it. But he didn't. I know Dan hasn't been playing as long as the other good players. Do you think maybe he hasn't learned that play yet? I would've asked him, only he took so long to play the hand there wasn't time."

"Do you remember the whole deal?" the Professor inquired, knowing she wouldn't and hoping she wouldn't try, since the attempt to reconstruct a half-remembered deal was always an exercise in futility.

"I wanted to show you after the game," said Corey. "I got the board, but you left before I could show you, so I copied it down like you said."

This was a pleasant surprise. His students often had a deal they wanted to discuss, but they rarely copied it out and they seldom remembered enough to have a sensible discussion.

Dummy
♠ A Q 9 8 4
♡ A 5 2
◇ J 4 2
♣ J 7

West (Christine)
♠ J 5 3 2
♡ 9
◇ A K 10 5
♣ 8 4 3 2

East (Corey)
♠ 10 7
♡ Q J 6 3
◇ Q 8 6 3
♣ K 9 5

South (Dan)
♠ K 6
♡ K 10 8 7 4
◇ 9 7
♣ A Q 10 6

The Professor was puzzled. The trump holding was almost identical to his example. With two sure diamond losers, the only way to make four hearts was to avoid two trump losers and that was easily done by taking the safety play in hearts. Looking at all four hands, the Professor could see no reason to reject the safety play. The fact that Dan had taken some time over the play suggested that he had considered the safety play and had imagined a phantom danger, which dissuaded him from making a play which was standard for all good players.

"This is an excellent illustration of our lesson, Corey. The only way the game can be made is with the safety play. On the other hand, Dan would not have played as he did without a good reason, so why don't you show him the deal, find out what he was thinking and then report back to the class."

Corey gulped and nodded assent. This was not what she had bargained for when she copied down the deal.

C H A P T E R

On Tuesday night after the game, Corey hung back as Dan and Clayton discussed their estimate of their game. Dan thought two and a half boards above average, but Clayton was sure it was better than that — more like three and a half boards, which was usually good enough for first.

Corey was shy about approaching Dan. She had played against him countless times and quickly lost the nervousness that came with him being a policeman. All the same, she had never really talked to him. It would have been easier to ask him at the time why he hadn't finessed the heart ten. Bringing it up a week later made it a much bigger deal. Still, she had opened her big mouth in class so now she had to do it.

As Clayton left the table, Corey rushed forward to catch Dan before he got up. "Dan, can I ask you about a hand from last week?"

"Sure, Corey, but I probably won't remember. Once we play a new game, I lose all the hands from the previous one." He paused momentarily. "Unless it's the four-heart hand I played against you?"

"That's it." Corey never failed to be impressed by the memory of the good players. Dan probably wouldn't even need the copy of the deal she had made, but she had it in her hand so she laid it on the table.

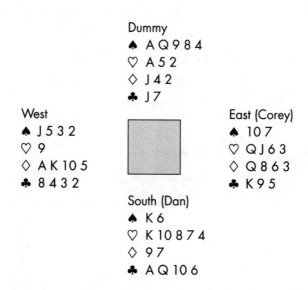

Dummy
♠ A Q 9 8 4
♡ A 5 2
◇ J 4 2
♣ J 7

West
♠ J 5 3 2
♡ 9
◇ A K 10 5
♣ 8 4 3 2

East (Corey)
♠ 10 7
♡ Q J 6 3
◇ Q 8 6 3
♣ K 9 5

South (Dan)
♠ K 6
♡ K 10 8 7 4
◇ 9 7
♣ A Q 10 6

"Yes, I lost some sleep over that one. I'll bet the Professor's been teaching safety plays." He could tell by the slight widening of her eyes that he was right. "I did consider finessing with the heart ten. But it seemed to me at the time there was another danger that was more likely than the four-one trump split."

He started to explain and then, realizing that Corey was not going to be able to follow the explanation using the diagram, he pulled the cards from the last board he had played and rearranged the cards to produce the hands in Corey's diagram. "I was worried about the shortage of entries to dummy. Note that once the trumps are gone, I can only get to the dummy in spades and I can only do that once if I want to take a trick first with the king in my hand. Playing the ace of trumps and then low to my ten is a safety play only if I can afford to lose the second trump trick to the person on my left. Christine, wasn't it?"

Corey nodded.

"Christine cashed her two top diamonds and then made an inspired switch to a small spade, which I won in my hand with the king. With hindsight, I know now that the safety play would have worked. But most of the time Christine would have two or three trumps to the queen or jack. Observe what happens if this is actually the case — if the trumps split three-two and I lose the second trump to Christine on my left." Dan played the cards from the hands, which were face up on the table.

Dummy

♠ A Q 9 4
♡ 5
♢ J
♣ J 7

South (Dan)

♠ 6
♡ K 7 4
♢ —
♣ A Q 10 6

"Christine is on lead and I've lost three tricks. In this hypothetical case, there is one trump outstanding, which I can draw with my heart king. But if Christine uses up my only sure entry to dummy by leading another spade, then I have problems. I need the club finesse, but even if the club king is onside, you will cover the jack with your king, so my club six will be a loser. I can't draw the last trump because that would put me in my hand with no way to cash my good spades or take the club finesse. I could try to cash a spade, pitching a club and hoping that whoever had the last trump also had a spade. If that worked, there would still be the club finesse to take before drawing trumps. Or I could take the club finesse and ruff the third round of clubs and hope that whoever held the remaining trump hadn't started with a doubleton club."

Corey had followed the first part of this, but by the time he got to the club finesse she was coasting along in neutral. She regrouped as Dan continued. "Now look again at the hypothetical case where the trumps split three-two and instead of taking the finesse, I just play off the ace and king of trumps. That brings us to almost the same position.

Dummy
♠ A Q 9 4
♡ 5
◊ J
♣ J 7

South (Dan)
♠ 6
♡ 10 7 4
◊ —
♣ A Q 10 6

"The difference here is that I've lost two tricks with a sure trump loser in one of your hands. Now I can play the spades from the top. If the spades don't split and if one of you trumps in before I play the queen of spades to pitch my little club, then the heart five in dummy will be an entry to take my pitch and then take the club finesse. If the spades do split, I won't even have to take the club finesse."

Corey had been keeping up this time. "So the safety play would not have been so safe if the hearts had split three-two."

"That's right. In fact, finessing the heart ten shouldn't be called a safety play in this situation because it doesn't guarantee the contract and, as near as I could figure out, it doesn't even increase the chances of success. The reason I took so long is I was trying to estimate the percentages. After I played the heart ace and then low from dummy with you following low, I had seen all the spots — the only remaining hearts were the queen and jack. I figured the odds were three-to-one that Christine had at least one of them. Fran says it's actually five-to-one — I haven't had a chance yet to get her to show me how she gets that. Since Christine was probably going to win if I finessed and since I would then have to give up on the possibility of using my spades to avoid the club finesse, the safety play didn't look so safe. I finally decided that finessing to protect against Q-J-x-x on my right was more dangerous than playing my heart king and hoping for a three-two split.

There was also the possibility that with Q-J-x-x, you might have split your honors, creating a different set of problems. Since you hadn't and since I didn't want Christine to win, the safety play didn't look safe to me."

Corey had not taken in all the details, but she had the general idea. "So you were not so much thinking about safety as you were trying to figure which was the least of two dangers — kind of like Elsie when the smoke alarm was screaming and she had to decide whether to go the slow way down through the canyon with her house on fire or the fast way across the trestle when the train might come."

"Smoke alarm?" Dan's tone was as casual as a cat that has just spied a bird landing closer to the cat than was good for the health of the bird.

"You know, the day she...." Corey's voice got softer and trailed away as she realized she was speaking of something Dan didn't already know.

"The day she died?" asked Dan.

Corey nodded. Now she had put her foot in it. Dan was going to ask her questions she had no reason not to answer but would just as soon not. Not that it mattered now, since everybody knew Angie was pregnant, and it wouldn't be too hard to figure out what she and Kevin had been doing that day. But she felt self-conscious. Besides, if Dan didn't know about the alarm, then she had been withholding important information. When Angie told her about the alarm, Corey wondered why she hadn't already heard about it. She had intended to dig out the memorial *Chronicle* to see if it was mentioned there, but had not gotten around to it.

"You want to know about the smoke alarm."

It was more a statement than a question. Dan nodded. She continued, "I didn't find out until months after the accident. I figured the investigators would already know something like that and even if they didn't, what did it matter four months later? You see, Angie was out there when it happened, with Kevin Blakely, and she wasn't even supposed to be seeing Kevin, let alone off with him in a blueberry patch. She didn't say anything about it and she somehow managed to get Kevin to keep his mouth shut too. Then she found out she was pregnant and she kept quiet about that too for a while, but that's the sort of secret you can't keep forever."

"So Angie and Kevin heard the smoke alarm go off?"

"Yes, they were out of sight of the house, but they heard the alarm. When they cleared the ridge, there was Elsie, running along the edge of the ravine. She hesitated for a split second at the tracks then turned and headed across the bridge. That ravine's deep, so she must have figured to save maybe as much as five minutes."

"Angie said she just put her head down with her legs pumping real fast, just like she'd been doing it all her life, which maybe she had considering she'd lived by that bridge from the time she was born."

Dan nodded encouragingly.

"Then there was the train, coming through the rock cut. Angie said the engineer gave her a blast and she sort of broke stride and then kept on even faster, heading straight for that train. Maybe when she was a kid she had the idea that if she ever got caught on that bridge she could jump into the creek because just before she met the train she jumped. Angie and Kevin started out to help. When they got to the edge of the canyon, they could see that she'd hit the creek. It's not as deep as it used to be and it was the middle of the summer, so there wasn't enough water to break her fall, let alone enough to dive into. By that time, the train was almost stopped and it was obvious somebody was going to help Elsie, so Angie grabbed Kevin and they kept out of sight."

"When did the smoke alarm stop?"

"I don't know. What makes you think it stopped?" Dan was starting to explain when Corey saw the answer to her own question.

"Of course. You didn't know about the alarm, so it must have stopped."

"Do you think Angie would be willing to talk to me about what she saw?" asked Dan.

"She might like that. I think it's been on her mind that she was a witness and didn't tell somebody official like."

"I'm not an official person any more, but maybe I'll do anyway. If I were to drop by to lend you a bridge book, would you invite me in for coffee?"

Corey flushed. Discussing bridge with Dan would just give her another chance to stick her foot in her mouth somehow. He was bridge royalty, a nice man, but he made her nervous.

The fact that Dan was an eligible male, even if he was older than her, had little to do with it. Corey was comfortable with men. Since Brian's death, she had been avoiding serious relationships because of the children, especially Angie, the youngest. They had been very fond of their father. She had resolved not to get involved until they were grown up. This resolve was made easier by the fact that even after twenty years of marriage, she was still in love with Brian. By the time she stopped mourning, she had grown accustomed to making her own decisions and was in no hurry to change.

Corey agreed to call Dan sometime later in the week when Angie was going to be in for the evening. As Dan was gathering up the demonstration cards, Katie saved her from further discussion.

"Dan and Clayton had a big game. Well done, Dan. You and I didn't do so well," she said, turning to Corey.

Corey and Katie left the hall together. At her car, Corey asked, "Would you like a ride?"

"It's just a few blocks. Clears my head." Instead of stopping to chat, Katie had already started down the street.

What's with her? thought Corey. It wasn't like Katie to go charging off like that. As Corey was pulling out, she waited for Russell to walk past. She rolled her window down and said goodnight, but he didn't seem to notice. *This is curious*, thought Corey. She watched. Katie turned around before she got to the end of the block. Corey could hear her clearly as she said, "Russell, if you're going to be my guardian angel, why don't you step up here and walk beside me."

They turned to the right. Corey was not a snoop, but this was too much to resist. She eased up to the corner, pulled over to the curb and watched. Katie's house was two and a half blocks away. They stopped briefly in front of her house and then both went in.

* * * * *

Dan called Corey the next day to make sure that Angie would be home in the evening and that it was okay for him to stop by.

Angie knew he was coming, but not that she was the one he wanted to see. She watched her mother with a mixture of irritation and amusement. Angie had a test to study for, the baby in her belly kept kicking to remind her that she was pregnant, and there was her mother bustling around straightening things that were already straight just because old Dan Cogan was coming over to drop off a bridge book. Her thirty-eight year old mother was acting like a schoolgirl before her first date.

Still, she was being very nice about this baby. Corey had tried to keep Angie from getting serious about Kevin, but when Angie got pregnant, her mother had taken it in stride. She did just one 'I told you so' and then said, "Okay, it's done. What do you want to do now?" She encouraged Angie to stay in school for the year and a half it would take to get her grade twelve and offered to help with the baby if Angie decided to keep it.

Kevin wanted to get married right away. He would quit school and get a job to support them. Angie was torn — she was crazy about Kevin, couldn't imagine marrying anyone else, but wasn't sure she was ready yet to become anybody's wife. Since there weren't any jobs anyway, and since neither her mother nor his parents were encouraging them to get married, they were both still in school.

The doorbell rang and her mother invited Dan in for the coffee she had started as soon as she saw his car pull into the driveway. Dan sat down in the kitchen and Angie could hear them talking about bridge hands in the same foreign language her mother used when on the phone to her bridge-playing friends. The words were all recognizably English, but the meanings were changed so it was impossible to understand what they were talking about.

Not that she cared.

Had Angie been listening carefully, she would have realized that the jargon used by Dan was somewhat more extensive than the one Corey shared with Rita, Katie and Christine. Angie had no use for card games. It was okay for her mother — she was glad Corey had this activity — but she couldn't see the fun of sitting for hours in a smoke-filled room to win some rubbers or whatever.

When the coffee was ready, Angie went to the kitchen. She knew Dan by reputation. Not a bad guy for a cop. She had seen him around town, but if he was going to come calling on her mother, then she wanted a closer look.

"Angie, this is Mr. Cogan."

"Dan Cogan." Dan smiled at Angie. "When I retired from the department, I started using my first name again. I know your mother through bridge, which is very democratic — everybody competes on a first-name basis."

Angie nodded, but remained silent. She had no intention of calling him Dan and she did not know how to go about asking what she most wanted to know — that is, what was his interest in her mother?

"Corey mentioned that you witnessed the Elsie Carmichael accident."

Angie nodded again. "I was a little nervous about not telling the police, but Mom said you thought it was okay." Angie wondered momentarily if Dan had come over to see her rather than her mother. Her mom hadn't said anything about that, and he was retired from the department, so there wouldn't be any reason for him to be nosing around.

Dan, for his part, didn't want her to get the idea it was okay for her to judge what was relevant to a police investigation. "We didn't know about the smoke alarm. That explains why Elsie was on the trestle. From a criminal point of view, I don't see how that raises any red flags, but you really should have reported what you saw."

Angie felt her face go red and looked down at her feet. "Yeah, I guess."

"There's one thing I'm curious about. Did you notice when the smoke alarm stopped?"

Angie was startled. "I don't remember it stopping." Then, as she thought back to the scene, still vivid in her mind, she continued, "I guess it must have stopped because I'm sure it wasn't going when the train people were down in the canyon."

"Was there any smoke?"

"No. I know that for sure because when Mrs. Carmichael was running for the bridge, Kevin said we should go and help. I looked across the canyon and there was no smoke, so I stopped him. Our smoke alarm goes off all the time and it's never anything serious."

"Were you aware of any activity over at Hamilton House before you heard the smoke alarm?"

"No, we were back by the pond and we didn't even know she was on our side. About ten minutes before it all happened, there was a car horn that honked one long blast and then two short ones, like a signal. I remember that because, well, we hadn't started picking yet, so we decided we'd better get moving."

* * * * *

Dan sat down opposite Phil at Mary's Lunch.

"Who are you playing with next Tuesday?" asked Phil.

Dan hesitated slightly. "I have a game with Corey Loucks."

"Ah, widow Loucks. A little severe perhaps, but she has a nice smile."

Dan could see that he was going to be subjected to innuendos unless he provided an explanation. Corey was barely average in bridge ability and would not usually get asked by one of the better players. "I stopped by her place two nights ago to drop off a couple of bridge books. She's taking the Professor's advanced course. I figured I ought to have a game with her to give her a chance to play opposite someone who actually does what the Professor teaches them to do."

Phil looked at him quizzically with just the trace of a smile. Dan was telling the truth, but it was not the whole truth. He could see that Phil knew there was something he wasn't saying. With the half-truth, Dan was just digging himself in deeper. He valued his friendship with Phil too much to leave him with an impression that could be embarrassing, for one or both of them, somewhere down the road. He had been planning to talk to Clayton first, but he changed his mind.

"A week ago Thursday, Corey made a stray comment about Elsie's leap from the trestle. It turns out that her daughter Angie was a witness."

Phil took a few seconds to digest this. "Why didn't Angie come forward at the time?" he asked, realizing as he spoke what the answer would be. "Okay, never mind that. So you needed an excuse to go over and quiz Angie because you're not an official investigator anymore. You're not going to tell me it was really a suicide?"

"Just the opposite. Elsie was running across the bridge because their smoke alarm went off."

"Goddamn smoke alarms. I wonder how often they go off when nothing's happening for every time there's actually a fire. Still I guess

I'd sooner hear it was an accident than suicide. I was always fond of Elsie and wouldn't like to think she got so bored with life she decided to play chicken with that freight."

"Elsie must have known the freight was due, and even though something set off the alarm, there was no smoke coming from the house. Why do you suppose she took the chance?" asked Dan.

"Maybe she had one of her dogs out in the summer kitchen. She treated those dogs like family. Whenever one of them was sick or whelping, she'd bring it into the house. But how do you suppose she heard that alarm? It's near a quarter of a mile across that ravine. Those alarms are loud as hell if you're inside the house, but I doubt the sound would carry too far outside."

"This one was loud enough that Angie and Kevin heard it and they didn't have a sick dog to be worried about. Maybe the windows were open."

CHAPTER

"Hi Corey," said Mac, as Dan and Corey arrived at their table. "Where did you pick up this old geezer?"

Corey was of two minds about the banter. Though she was on a first-name basis with everyone in the club, for the first time many of the better players seemed too conscious of her presence. She sensed they were watching to see what Dan had noticed that they had missed.

Players like Mac, on the other hand, were noticed immediately by experts and novices alike. They all knew Mac, or, at least, they knew his reputation. Corey wished they were playing against someone else, even the Stinsons, because she was pretty sure that she and Dan were having a good game. Mac was the last person you wanted to play when you were doing well. He was not a top player, but he was unpredictable and lucky as all get out.

Mac was a tall, thin man who always looked as though he was thinking about a private joke. Mac had a reputation for being lucky that was already well established when he started to play duplicate. He was so lucky at the game of curling that even non-curlers knew of him. It seemed he could do no wrong on the curling rink. It wasn't that he was a superb skip or shot-maker. In fact, he often called an inferior shot and then came down the ice off the broom, wrong weight and sometimes even the wrong turn and his shot would end up doing something better than any plan he could have made. It was hard, even for top players, to cope with that kind of luck.

Mac was a better bridge player than anyone realized because, whenever possible, he put down to luck the tricks he acquired by skill. John MacIntosh was probably no luckier than the next person, but he had long ago observed that to be perceived as lucky was almost as effective as actually being lucky. When he was curling, he would occasionally call for the second-best or third-best shot and then aim for the best one. If he actually made his shot, it would be seen as incredibly lucky. His deflated opposition did not always play their best from that point onward. Some of his curling friends suspected him of not trying for the shot that he seemed to be calling, but he never admitted to it and the majority of curlers persisted in assuming he was lucky — there is a modicum of dignity, after all, in losing to the good luck of your opponent rather than to your own inferior skill.

There are fewer chances at bridge for the same sort of tactic. Mainly, he made unexpected bids and plays whenever he could do so without a great deal of risk. This kept his opponents off balance and when such maneuvers gained a trick, or even did no more than fail to cost him a trick, his reputation for being lucky was further enhanced.

Mac's favorite play came up so seldom that no one suspected him of doing it on purpose. Mac was unaware that it already had a name—the Grosvenor Gambit. Mac discovered it by accident in much the same way that the fictional Grosvenor discovered it (in a story by Frederick B. Turner published in *The Bridge World*). Both of them accidentally played the wrong card to a trick they could have won. This cost a trick, which came right back because declarer made a wrong assumption. Mac immediately recognized the potential this sort of accident had for enhancing his reputation for being lucky. The ideal situation came up less than once a year, but Mac was always on the lookout and spotted one on the first deal against Dan and Corey.

Corey opened the bidding one diamond. Dan responded one heart, Stan overcalled two clubs, Corey raised Dan to two hearts and Dan jumped to four hearts. Stan led the club king and Corey put down her hand as dummy.

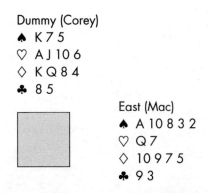

Dummy (Corey)
♠ K 7 5
♡ A J 10 6
◇ K Q 8 4
♣ 8 5

East (Mac)
♠ A 10 8 3 2
♡ Q 7
◇ 10 9 7 5
♣ 9 3

Mac could see that with two club tricks and his spade ace, they had three top tricks. Furthermore, if Stan continued with a third round of clubs, Mac would be able to overtrump dummy for the setting trick (unless Dan trumped in dummy with the heart ace).

Dan's hand was:

South (Dan)
♠ Q J 4
♡ K 9 8 4 2
◇ A 2
♣ Q 10 4

After Stan played king, ace and another club, Dan had a decision to make. Dan's queen was now the high club, but since Mac followed with the nine and then the three of clubs, Dan assumed he started with only two clubs and was preparing to trump this trick.

The difficulty was that with Mac you never knew for sure — he might play high-low, showing two cards in the suit, when he actually held three. If Mac was out of clubs, then Dan should trump high in dummy. But with which card? If Mac didn't have the heart queen, then dummy's ten or jack would be sufficient. If Mac had the heart queen, then he should trump with the heart ace and finesse against the queen. Since there was some possibility that Mac wasn't even out of clubs, Dan called for the heart jack.

Mac discarded the spade eight! Dan congratulated himself on a good guess. Mac obviously did not have the heart queen or he would have overtrumped. Dan crossed to his diamond ace and led the heart nine towards dummy, finessing against the queen in Stan's hand — a proven finesse now that he knew Mac didn't have the missing honor.

The proven finesse failed as Mac won with the queen and cashed his spade ace. The contract was down the same one trick it had been destined to go down from the moment Dan trumped with the heart jack. Mac resisted the urge to smile. The Grosvenor Gambit was a deception play that only worked against an opponent who was alert enough to draw logical conclusions from a failure to make an obvious play. There were deception plays that risked a trick in order to gain a trick. Such plays, by definition, were not Grosvenor Gambits. A Grosvenor was a silly play because it didn't gain a trick and it risked losing a trick that didn't have to be lost.

Very few players, even those who knew the play, ever did a Grosvenor Gambit on purpose, because it made the perpetrator of the gambit look incompetent. It was a rare bridge player who was willing to look bad in order to gain a slight psychological advantage. Mac was one of those rare people.

"Sorry, partner," said Mac at the end. "When Dan stopped and thought on the third round of clubs, I was so sure he was going to trump with the ace that I discarded the spade before I noticed he had trumped with the jack. Lucky for me he decided to finesse rather than play for the drop."

When it became apparent they had a nine-card heart fit, Corey was puzzled by Dan's play of the suit. She had been following the play, up to the point where Dan took the finesse, but had not grasped the significance of Mac's failure to overruff with the heart queen on the third round of clubs. "Why did you finesse?" she asked Dan. "I thought that with a nine-card fit you were supposed to play for the drop."

Dan remained silent for a moment in order to avoid being rude (if he had said what came first to mind, he would have been insulting both Corey and Mac). Corey was referring to the rule Eight ever, Nine never. This was a guide used by bridge teachers who were teaching basic play technique to beginners. It applied when a choice arose between finessing for the queen or playing for it to drop. It was comforting for the novice to have a rule to help with the decision.

In the present case, Dan had an ironclad guarantee that Mac did not have the heart queen, so the finesse through Stan was the proper play even though it broke the rule. Dan took a few deep breaths and then explained. "When Mac didn't overruff the dummy's heart jack, I assumed that he didn't have the queen. If you think you know the location of the queen, even if it's just a hunch, it is better to finesse for it than to play for the drop."

Corey felt like an ass. It was obvious. She should have kept her mouth shut until she thought the deal through. The traveling score slip for the board showed that most people had been in four hearts down the same one trick as Dan and Corey, so the result for the board was only slightly below average. Mac's little trick had gained him nothing on that board, but he had not expected anything. The payoff came on the following board when Dan's suppressed irritation caused him to miss an overtrick. It was a play that average players would miss, but it should have been routine for Dan. Below average again and on a board that would have been a tie for top.

Dan and Corey got up from Mac's table and had to wait a minute for the players at the next table to finish. Dan started to apologize for his lapse in concentration. Corey interrupted, "Do you think Mac did that on purpose?" Corey, embarrassed at her own gaffe, thought that Mac should have been even more embarrassed, but he seemed quite pleased with himself. Most players can't stand making a bad play, even when it turns out well.

"Why would he do that?" said Dan. "It didn't gain a thing."

"It got you upset. And then I asked a silly question which made matters worse, so you didn't play your best on the next deal."

Dan was surprised. She was probably wrong about Mac, but she was right about the table action. Corey's play was adequate, he thought. In fact, it was better than he had expected. And even though she was nowhere near expert level, her assessment of the climate at the table was very good — it augured well for her future as a bridge player.

"I doubt even Mac would do that on purpose. There's a story in *Bridge World* about a guy called Grosvenor who made such plays, but Mac's not a reader. Also, you'd have to be a little bit better than Mac to recognize the right situation and then pull it off without getting caught. Nevertheless, you're right about the effect. We lost some ground there, but we're still having a good game. With a little luck on the last four deals, we could still win."

Dan and Corey got back on track and finished strong. Their last two boards were against Clayton Carmichael and Phil Stinson.

On the first, Corey had to decide whether to lead fourth best from her best suit or to lead her doubleton suit and try to get a ruff. She chose her doubleton and it turned out to be the right decision this time — a tie for top with the other three pairs who set four spades. On the final board, she and Dan bid to a grand slam in clubs, which Corey had to play. Grand slams were rare and Corey was very nervous to be playing one against such good opposition.

The play was interesting but not difficult. She had to trump diamonds twice to set up dummy's fifth diamond for the thirteenth trick. Since the Professor had just done a lesson on setting up long suits, she got it right. Their grand slam scored well because many pairs had stopped in six, and a few had played in notrump, which made only twelve tricks.

Corey was elated. If she came first tonight, it would be just the second time in five years. In addition, this was the first time she had played with someone as good as Dan and she was very pleased that she had not let him down.

As they left the table, Dan asked Clayton if they could get together with him for a few minutes after the game. Clayton nodded. He raised an eyebrow to ask why, but Dan was off to join Corey at the scoreboard.

The big board where four people were entering scores was an innovation the Professor had brought back from Kingston in 1972. Before then, the director would enter the scores on a large sheet of paper and only those with good eyes and enough interest to shove into the crowd around the director could watch the scores as they were posted. Now they had two large blackboards (one each for North-South and East-West) with permanent lines corresponding to the master sheet. Several people could work on each board simultaneously. Posting was fast and the spectators could get out their personal scorecard and mark down their matchpoints on individual deals as they were being posted. As a result, most people waited to get their scores and placings.

Dan, who usually helped with the posting of scores, watched with Corey. "I think we're going to be alright," he said. "Nobody else seems to have had a big game."

Dan was right. When the results were totaled, Dan and Corey were well ahead of second place. This was just Corey's second win in the main section. Corey's first win, with Katie, had been a thrill, even though they'd won because they were remarkably lucky. That first had been handed to them. This win felt different. She and her partner had been lucky this time too, but luck was not the whole story — they had earned many of their good boards. To be more precise, Dan had earned them. Bridge, however, is a partnership game and she'd held her own. Dan even congratulated her several times on her play or defense. Most bridge players felt that their partner was holding them back — it was often said that any partnership was only as good as the weaker member. Corey, an open, generous person, was not entirely immune to the feeling that some of her partners were holding her back. This win with Dan was especially satisfying because it implied that she was better than her usual results would suggest.

All of Corey's regular partners congratulated her. Many of the other players went out of their way to say, "Nice game." Much of the satisfaction in winning was in knowing as you went along that you were playing well and that things were working as they should. But recognition was part of it too. Very few people, on the other hand, made a point of congratulating Dan. He won so often that he had ceased to receive special recognition for doing so.

Clayton fell into step with Dan and Corey as they left the hall. Dan suggested they meet at the Donut Shop for a coffee. Dan would sooner have taken Corey to the Cornerstone where they could celebrate their victory with the bridge players that usually went there after the game. Corey had agreed, however, that Clayton ought to be told about Elsie before it became general knowledge.

When they were settled and Clayton had repeated his congratulations to Corey, Dan said, "Corey's daughter Angie was picking blueberries the day that Elsie died. The reason that Elsie was running across the trestle was that the smoke alarm at your house had gone off."

Clayton didn't seem to know how to react at first, but then he looked stricken. "I never really believed she was committing suicide, but if it was the smoke alarm, then I'm to blame."

"How could that be?" asked Corey.

"She would never have heard the alarm across the canyon if I hadn't connected it to an outdoor speaker."

Dan raised his eyebrows. "Why would you do that?"

"One day last spring the alarm went off while Elsie was out in the garden and she didn't hear it. It was just some soup that was simmering that had boiled over, so no harm done, but it just about drove Cleopatra crazy. That is... or was... our best breeding female. She was in with a three-day-old litter. I hooked up a horn on the side of the house so if it ever happened again we could hear it out in the garden.

"Of course Elsie scarcely ever went across the canyon except in blueberry season, so I never even thought about what would happen if it went off when she was over there. She used to go across that trestle all the time, but I made her promise to stop doing it. She claimed there was no danger because she knew the freight schedule and besides she could put her ear to the track and tell if a train was coming. But it made me nervous, so I made her promise anyway. I guess with that smoke alarm going, she didn't stop to listen."

"Why would she take such a risk?" asked Dan. "You say the time it happened before there hadn't really been a fire. Were any of the dogs in the house this time?"

"Cleo and Brutus had some sort of infection, a minor thing really, but she had both of them in the back kitchen. There's something about those damn alarms that makes you automatically think the worst. The dogs were just like children to her — she was probably thinking about the house burning and them not able to get out."

"I guess there wasn't any fire," said Corey.

"No, it didn't even occur to me that the smoke alarm might have gone off. I should have known, because the dogs were nervous wrecks when I got back to the house. That was much later though and you know how animals are supposed to be psychic — I just figured they knew somehow about Elsie. There was a roast in the oven that I'd put in just before I left. It was overcooked by the time I got back, but there was no sign that it had been on fire. Maybe there was grease in the oven that smoked a little when the oven got up to temperature?"

"Wouldn't you have noticed something if there was burnt grease?" asked Corey.

"No, I just stuck the roast in the oven and turned it on and left. Had an appointment in town. I'd have set the timer, but it was just about the time it was supposed to go on anyway. The house may have smelled a little when I got back, but with a roast in the oven, I never thought twice about it." He frowned and looked down at his tightly clasped hands. He went a little pale as he said in a much quieter voice, "Besides, when I got back, there was a train stopped out just beyond the trestle and Elsie was at the bottom of the canyon. Even if the house had reeked, I wouldn't have noticed."

"The other thing Angie mentioned was a honk of your car horn. Do you remember why you did that?"

"We always did that. Anytime one of us was leaving in the car and the other person was outside somewhere, the person in the car would honk."

Nobody spoke for a few seconds and then Dan cleared his throat. "Did she know you were planning on leaving?"

"She was expecting me to go into town at four, but I didn't actually leave until twenty-five past."

Dan drummed his fingers on the table, thinking. Eventually he said, "So it's possible she assumed it was the wrong time, that she didn't expect the four-thirty train to be a danger to her, and that's why she ran across."

Clayton looked horrified. "Then it really is my fault."

He put his head in his hands, and Corey reached awkwardly across the table to pat his shoulder.

C H A P T E R

"I know," said Phil, "you just wanted to prove you could win with anybody."

Dan had just joined him at Mary's Lunch and Phil assumed that he would be gloating about his win with Corey the previous night. The good players usually played with each other and took their wins as a matter of course. It was a much greater challenge to win with a weak player.

"It's true, of course," said Dan, "but Corey deserves some of the credit. She has potential."

"You think it's time the rest of us took a turn."

"Yes, it is. Lessons and reading are good, but she needs somebody across the table who's doing the same thing."

"Okay, okay," said Phil, "I'll ask her for a game." It was an unspoken rule that the better players should ask up-and-coming players for a game. The rule was not always observed. It was no fun to play with someone who made bad bids or plays at crucial moments and argued they had done the right thing. With someone like Corey, attractive and deferential, it would be easy. And unlike Dan, he had been aware of Corey and had been intending to ask her for a game anyway.

"We missed you at the Cornerstone." Phil's statement was an inquiry.

"You no doubt missed Clayton as well. As you know, Corey had information about Elsie's death that we thought he should know."

Phil waited expectantly. Dan sat for a minute as though he had said his piece.

"Out with it," said Phil, "or I'll have to start smoking again. Actually, I might start smoking again anyway, but I certainly will if you don't tell me what Angie told you and how Clayton took it."

When Dan got to the part about Clayton accepting responsibility for the false alarm, Phil interrupted, "Good ploy. Accepting responsibility makes him seem innocent."

"If you like that, you're really going to like the next part," said Dan and told him about the horn signals and how Clayton pleaded guilty to misleading Elsie about the time.

"Good Lord," said Phil, "He did two things which work together to put Elsie out on that trestle at the worst possible time and he cops to both of them. Either he's utterly innocent or he's devious as hell, guilty as sin, and smarter than I would ever have given him credit for being. Which way are you leaning?"

"I've always felt there should be a presumption of innocence until you discover something that can't be reconciled. We've got nothing here for which there's no innocent explanation. If I was the official investigator, I'd have a tough time convincing my superiors that I ought to stay on the case."

"You don't sound happy about it."

"It's too neat. A case with no loose ends is very rare."

"You had lots of loose ends last week. Were you happier then?"

"Right. I was uneasy when we had no explanation for Elsie charging that train. Now we have one. Case closed."

"So Clayton had nothing to do with it."

"I didn't say that."

"What did you say then?" asked Phil.

"In every investigation where you suspect foul play but have no evidence of foul play, you reach a point where you have no expectation of discovering something about the case that would resolve the matter, one way or the other. It becomes a cold case."

"So you don't think we should run it past somebody else. Say Kit? Elsie was his cousin, after all. Maybe she said something to him that would create a loose end for you."

"She might have done," said Dan, "but I don't want to give Kit the idea we're not completely satisfied. Discretion is a foreign word to Kit. Clayton is probably innocent. If we put a bee in Kit's bonnet, there's no telling where he'd go with it."

"Maybe we could sound him out without implicating Clayton."

Dan thought about it a while. "That might work. We could wait until the next time he joins us for lunch and then fill him in on the alarm business without suggesting that Clayton had any active part in it. Which shouldn't be too hard since we have no reason to think he did."

CHAPTER

Jake Harden turned off the alarm on the first ring at 4:30 a.m. Susan didn't stir. Her internal clock was programmed to ignore Jake's alarm. Her own alarm was set for 6:30 and she would wake in time to turn it off before it rang.

When he wasn't playing bridge, or researching and writing the history of Pemberton, Jake ran a mixed farm, five miles north of Pemberton, which had been in his family since the beginning of the century. In the dim light of pre-dawn, Jake went directly from his bed to the barn to milk the cows. When he finished milking, he would have breakfast with Susan and Jenny and then return to the barn to finish his morning chores. Most farmers, like Jake, started their day very early, because the two milkings had to be timed to be twelve hours apart. Milking time had to be very regular or milk production would suffer.

It was standard practice for dairy farmers to start their morning milking early enough that they could do their second milking before supper — which left their evenings free. In order to have a social life, they had to maintain this schedule even if all they wanted was an occasional evening away from the farm. Changing the schedule, even for one day, would affect production.

What Jake could do, once in a while, was cheat by a quarter of an hour. Accordingly, on Tuesday afternoons, Jake started the milking a few minutes early, finished at 6:45, and left cleanup for his daughter Jenny in order to be able to shower, grab a quick bite, and get into Pemberton for the bridge game at 7:30.

On this morning in May, when breakfast was over, Jenny off to school, and the morning chores done, Jake headed for town to pick up a part for the harrow, which was waiting for him in Pemberton. Usually, when there was something to be welded, he would wait at

Russell's Welding and Machine Repair until it was done. At this time of year, there was often a line-up and yesterday had looked like a township meeting at Russell's. Instead of waiting, he had left his two pieces of harrow there. A phone call after breakfast this morning confirmed that the welding was done and the two pieces were one functional piece again.

As he crested the gentle hill going down into Oak Valley, he saw an approaching car swerve, brake and pull over onto the shoulder. Jake slowed down and pulled up opposite. The driver of the other car was just getting out. It was Christine, the artist.

The reason for her sudden swerve and stop was clear. Christine had run down a raccoon with kits. Tears ran down her face as she surveyed the carnage. She had somehow managed, very much against the law of averages, to run over the mother and both of her kits.

Jake rolled down his window. "Never seen a family group out this early in the year. Unfortunate for you and the raccoons, but Bob Kendrick thanks you," said Jake. He got out of his truck and pointed at the newly seeded field beside the road. "He grows a market crop of sweet corn and these guys keep taking more than their share."

Christine did not look comforted. The mother raccoon lifted her head and hissed at them. "She's alive!" said Christine.

"Her back's broke," said Jake. "Notice how she's moving her front paws but not her back ones. We'd best put her out of her misery."

He went back to his truck and took a small baseball bat from behind the seat. As he advanced on the raccoon, Christine watched with a mixture of alarm and distaste. ("He always seemed kind at bridge," she said when she called her mother in Toronto. "But he looked like a brute when he swung that bat. I could never have done it. On the other hand, I've been unable to think of a more humane way of dealing with that poor animal.") The bat came down sharply on the skull of the mother raccoon. Her body heaved and a part of her side detached itself, moved a foot away from the body and then scurried back to the side of the dead mother.

"Another kitten!" exclaimed Christine, leaping forward.

"Don't touch," said Jake, holding out his free hand to restrain her. "That little tyke is no kitten. Given a chance he'll take your hand off."

"What will happen to him?"

"He won't survive on his own. The best thing we can do for him..." said Jake, raising the bat.

"Don't you dare," said Christine, jumping in front of him, arms raised. "Do you carry that thing around so you can club little animals?" ("Never took much notice of her at bridge," Jake told Susan that night, "but when she got between me and that raccoon, eyes flashing, breasts jumping, she sure was something.")

Jake looked at the bat. It had a swatch of red on the barrel. "Belongs to my daughter. She's got a regular sized one now, but I guess I better wash it off so I don't have to explain what I used it for."

They turned their attention back to the kit, which was alternately hissing at them and hiding its head in its mother's fur. "Too old to make it a pet," said Jake. "It's already got the wild in it."

"What do you mean, 'got the wild in it'?"

"Once they get old enough to get around and go on field trips with their mother, their ways get set and you can't tame them."

"How do you know? Have you ever tried taming a raccoon?"

"I got better things to do. It's just something everybody knows."

"Well, I don't know it," said Christine. She went to the back of her station wagon, lifted the lid, and pulled out a carrying cage.

"Jesus, you come prepared too, don't you? Guess you never know when you'll run down a mama raccoon."

"I had a cat," she said as she put the cage down and unlatched the door.

"Just a sec." Jake went back to the truck and took out a pair of heavy leather gloves with gauntlets to protect the wrists. "Use these. It'll be a little harder for him to take off a finger. But be careful. Even with the gloves, you can get scratched or bitten. Not a chance I'd take, even if I was partial to raccoons, which I'm not. A few scratches wouldn't be so bad, but the needle you have to get from the doctor is a real doozy. You sure you want to do this?"

Christine put on the gloves and slowly approached the kitten, making cooing noises to reassure it. The tiny raccoon pressed into the body of its mother. All of a sudden the kit made a move to escape. It was fast, but Christine was expecting this and she was faster. In one swift motion she picked up the kit, stuffed it into the cage, slipped her hands out of the gloves and closed the cage door.

"That was right smart," said Jake in admiration. The gloves remained with the kit in the cage. "Those were old gloves anyway. They now belong to you and Rocky."

"Rocky?"

"What else would you call a raccoon? Rocky will do until you think of something better."

Christine looked down at her hand where blood was welling up from a tiny puncture in her forefinger. There was more blood on her middle finger.

"Damn," said Jake, "he got you after all. Well, you better check in with the vet, to see if Rocky has any little critters that'd make him and you itch. And while you're there, you can call Doc Shaver and arrange for your shots."

The tiny bandit hissed at both of them and tried to hide behind the leather gloves.

C H A P T E R

Phil and Dan had just placed first in the weekly game and parked beside one another outside the Cornerstone. Despite their five years of friendship, they only played duplicate together a few times each year. There was just the one club game each week and both had prior obligations to other partners.

"We should play more often," said Dan. "Maybe we could go up to the Soo once in a while."

"Sure," said Phil, "as long as we don't try to do it too often. One late night in the middle of the week is about all I can handle without falling asleep on the job."

"I was thinking if we got Kit and a few others and gave Kit gas money plus a little to take us in his van, then we could discuss hands as we drove back."

Kit owned and drove Pemberton's only taxi. Even though Kit had the local business all to himself, it wasn't a full time job. Just about everybody on the North Shore owned or had access to a vehicle, so there wasn't much call for taxis. Fortunately for Kit, and perhaps for Pemberton too, since a town without a cab is not much of a town, Kit was independently wealthy. That is to say, he inherited an income from his mother that was sufficient in her day for a comfortable living. While the value had decreased due to inflation, it was still almost enough to keep Kit solvent. He just needed a small supplementary income to get by. Anybody in Pemberton who needed a taxi made an appointment. And everybody knew there was no point in trying to get an appointment on Tuesday nights during the bridge game.

One of Kit's regular fares was Gary Marshall out on the Plummer Road. He had been in a wheelchair since he rolled his tractor in 1974. The Marshalls had a van with a lift for the chair, but Ruth took night classes in the Soo on Tuesday nights. When Kit bought a new cab in 1979, he got a van with a lift. Grace Jones down on River Street and Millie Park over at the Red Castle also took advantage of his new service from time to time. Taking Gary home after bridge meant that Kit was always the last to join the group at the Cornerstone.

"It's a forty-five minute drive. If we finished discussing the hands by the time we got back to Pemberton, it would make for an earlier night than most of our Tuesdays," concluded Dan.

"Okay, let's try it," said Phil. "And when you're checking that out with Kit, you might ask why he hasn't been around at lunch time. Ever since we decided to get his take on the Elsie situation, he's been the invisible man. Sometimes he's around so regular you wish he'd get a job. Then when you want him he disappears."

"I'll ask him to meet us for lunch tomorrow," said Dan. They went into the Cornerstone, crossed to the bar and ordered drinks. Already seated at the long table in the corner were Fran, Rose, Clayton, Mac and Jake. Kevin, Barry and Christine were just arriving.

Bridge was the only topic of conversation at these gatherings after the weekly game, and almost all of that conversation was about the deals that had just been played. Sometimes there were special deals that got discussed immediately, but usually they took them in numerical order starting with board one. For each board, everybody consulted their personal scorecard and announced the contract and result at their table. Occasionally that would end the discussion.

More often there would be comments. Mac would ask, "Does anyone remember the dummy?" Fran or Dan would say, "Yes, it was ten fourth, king queen tight, ace ten fifth, small double." This would usually be enough to jog Mac's memory, "Oh yes, I remember, Mary led the three of hearts and Jake wrapped up five." "We should have been so lucky... they led a club against us."

The Professor usually arrived somewhere between boards five and ten. If there was a deal he had missed that he particularly wanted to go over, he would wait until they went through all the rest and then get them to go back to his deal. Kit usually came in shortly after the Professor and if there was one he wanted to discuss he would want to get to it immediately. Sometimes the others acquiesced. Sometimes they ignored him.

Kit had never developed a memory for bridge equal to that of other players of his ability and experience. When there was a particular deal he wanted to discuss, he got the board out after the game, before he left the club, and wrote down the hands.

On this evening, Kit stomped in, got a draft at the bar, and pushed up to the table in a manner that insisted that everyone stop and pay attention. "That Katie Burton ought to be committed. She's so stupid she's a danger to society." He tossed a hand written in large bold letters onto the table.

♠ Q J 9   ♡ 7   ◇ A K Q J 10 8 6 2   ♣ 3

"Rita opens one diamond on your right." Kit waited expectantly.

"I jumped to five diamonds," said Jake.

"Three notrump," said Dan.

"Of course," said Kit, ignoring Jake. "Now Dodo Burton on your left jumps to five clubs and that comes back to you." Kit waited again.

"Bet you wish you'd bid five diamonds in the first place," said Jake.

"Pass," said Phil.

"You're kidding, right?" said Kit, still ignoring Jake. "Do you think five clubs is going down?

"No, I figure she's void in diamonds and I don't want to push her into slam."

"Okay, so you know the hand. But these people don't bid slams just because you push them around. You can push them into game but not to slam."

When Kit said 'these people' he was referring to steady players of medium ability whom he felt he had a right to expect to be predictable.

"I bid five diamonds," he continued, "and she does take the push to six clubs. Now what?"

"I bought it for five diamonds doubled," said Jake.

"Leave well enough alone?" offered Dan.

"Yeah, sure. It probably makes for a top. So what have you got to lose? I bid six diamonds and she promptly goes to seven clubs. It's bullet proof. Not even Dodo Burton can find a way to lose a trick."

"Now tell me, what was she thinking? She was willing to play in five clubs and she takes the push to seven rather than a sure plus and probable top by doubling six diamonds. Assuming she's capable of thought, what the hell was she thinking?"

"If you wait until Friday, you'll find out," said Dan.

"What! You think she'll use that hand in her stupid column? Not a chance! She plays the fool sometimes, but she never admits to criminal stupidity. Even though she's the worst player in the club, she doesn't go out of her way to look stupid."

"You said last week the honor of worst player went to Russell."

"Russell's bad, I give you that. But he knows he's bad. And you know he's bad. So he can't hurt you too much. The thing about Burton is she sometimes seems to have half a brain and lulls you into a false sense of security. And then she turns so stupid, nobody's safe."

Kit usually closed the pub, but he had a 6 o'clock pickup, so he downed his beer and stormed off.

"I'll give two-to-one odds," said Dan, to the company at large, "that the hand will be in Friday's *Chronicle* and that Kit will look more foolish than Katie."

He got no takers. "Why didn't you float that bet while Kit was here? We all could have cashed in," said Phil.

"Could have," said Dan, "but I'm playing with him next Tuesday and it's going to be bad enough he's the subject of the column without making him pay cash for it as well."

"What tack do you think Jay will take?" asked Rose.

"Damned if I know. The only thing we can be sure of is she'll call him an expert and it will come out sounding like a handicap."

THE PEMBERTON CHRONICLE

Friday, May 27, 1983

THE JAY'S NEST
by Jane Seabrook

Dealer: North
Neither Vul.

```
              ♠ A
              ♡ AK54
              ◇ 9743
              ♣ A652
♠ 108654                    ♠ QJ9
♡ 109832                    ♡ 7
◇ 5                         ◇ AKQJ10862
♣ 94                        ♣ 3
              ♠ K732
              ♡ QJ6
              ◇ —
              ♣ KQJ1087
```

West	North	East	South
	1◇	3NT	5♣
pass	pass	5◇	6♣
pass	pass	6◇	7♣
all pass			

Opening lead: ◇5

Granddaddy Fenton, my mother's father, had a horse called Duke that could find his way home from any place, in any weather. When it was too dark or too foggy to see where they were going, Granddad didn't have to worry. He knew Duke would find the way. If Granddad felt like taking a nap on his way home from town, all he had to do was let the reins go slack and Duke would take over. When they arrived home Duke would stop at the barn door and stamp and snort until Granddad disconnected the carriage, removed the harness and led Duke to his stall. Many people had horses like Duke. Drinking and driving was no problem in those days — the drunks knew enough to let their horses drive.

Sometimes at the bridge table, when I don't have the slightest idea what I should do, I wish I had a horse like Duke. Most of the time I muddle through as best I can, but once in a while a horse steps up and I hand over the reins. For example, suppose I'm playing a hand and somebody tries to draw my trumps. If that somebody is an expert, so I can count on them to do what's right for them, then I look right sharp for ruffs, even if I'd not been planning any.

Not all experts are reliable. The Duck is always a mystery. Kit McCrea, on the other hand, always goes for the main chance. One could wish for no more dependable horse than Kit.

Rita opened one diamond and as I waited for Kit to pass, I wondered whether I should bid one spade to show my weak major or two clubs to show my strong minor.

But Kit didn't pass. He bid three notrump!

What should I do now? Four spades might be right but was too much of a gamble. Four clubs would be better, but would Rita take another bid? And what was Kit up to anyway? There surely weren't enough points in the deck for him to have a three notrump bid? Maybe he had a long running suit. The experts do that sometimes, you know. Then, if their partner has one or two stoppers, they get in and run that long suit.

I never think of three notrump myself when I have a long running suit. But if that's what Kit was doing, where was his suit?

Rita had bid diamonds and I had stoppers in each of the other suits. Sometimes it's impossible to figure out an expert, even one like Kit, so I decided to just bid five clubs and hope for the best.

Then Kit bid five diamonds and it became clear that Kit had a running diamond suit after all. And he was sacrificing.

I hadn't been sure I could make five clubs, but since Kit was sacrificing, he thought I could. And in matters like this, I trust his judgment more than my own.

If he was bent on sacrificing I would have to double. Then the Professor (a pretty good horse himself) passed by on his way for a coffee and I had another thought. The Professor is always saying that if partner has no points opposite your void, then such a void is more valuable.

It can be worth as much as ten points. Maybe this is true, but I always had trouble seeing why the Professor made such a big fuss about it — it seemed like useless bridge trivia to me. How would you know whether partner had points in your void without taking a walk around the table?

But here it was. I had a void in diamonds and my good horse Kit had just told me my partner had no points in that void. It wasn't much wonder I could make five clubs. With all those extra points for the void, I could probably make six clubs and maybe even seven clubs. I hate to bid slams without aces, but Rita had to have her points somewhere.

I decided to put my faith in Kit's judgment. What are experts for? He thought I could make five clubs and he didn't even know about my diamond void, so I must be able to make six clubs. When I bid six clubs and Kit bid six diamonds, I thought, "Yes, I was right. Kit thought I could make six clubs." And he still didn't know about my diamond void. So I bid seven. Who needs to be smart when you've got a horse like Kit?

C H A P T E R

When Dan entered Mary's Lunch at noon the following Wednesday, the first thing Phil said was: "He seemed to take it well."

"I swear at every table, the first thing we heard was 'Howdy Duke.' It would have gotten under my skin, but Kit seemed to thrive on it. You know how Kit likes to be the center of attention. I guess for him there's no such thing as bad attention. Just good attention and really good attention. When you think about it, Duke's not such a bad name. Sort of makes him the John Wayne of bridge."

"Did you ask Kit to join us for lunch?"

"He said he'd come today. I didn't get a chance to talk to him at the Cornerstone last week, so I mentioned it last night."

They finished their lunch and were nursing coffees when Kit finally arrived. Dan was not smoking a cigarette in deference to Phil's abstinence.

"Howdy Duke," said Phil.

"Stuff it, Phil," said Kit without rancor. "What's the mystery? I've just got a few minutes. My business has started to interfere with my free time."

"Okay," said Dan. "It's about Elsie and why she was on that trestle. Since she was your cousin, I thought you'd want to know," said Dan.

"It would appear she was running across the trestle because the smoke alarm had gone off."

"Jesus!" said Kit. Everyone was silent for a minute. "She was like a big sister to me. When my father died, me and my mom went to live with Uncle Bill and Cousin Elsie. I was just three. Elsie was seven and treated me like her personal doll for as long as I put up with it."

"Did she ever say anything that would suggest she and Clayton were having trouble?" asked Dan.

"Like what?"

"I dunno. You know, anything at all. Clayton says he warned her many times about walking across the trestle." Dan paused. "If they were having trouble, maybe she did it just to show him. Or maybe she was depressed and didn't care if the train came or not."

"No, nothing like that. We talked every week or so and I never noticed any depression. Clayton was always a little bugged she didn't give him control of her inheritance, but she didn't let it bother her."

"Clayton is still a little bugged on that issue because of Elsie's will," continued Kit. "I think he feels too much is going to the Brickworks museum. I'm supposed to get a new van, but I'll have to wait until the museum dispute is settled."

"Didn't Mary Garson get an annuity?" said Phil. "I thought that had already started."

"Yes, that was mentioned in the will, but there must have been some sort of special provision because it started immediately. I think maybe it was already bought and paid for and was to kick in the day Elsie died. So it wasn't part of Elsie's estate. In fact, now I think about it, that was what bugged him most at the reading of the will. He felt that the way it was set up implied a lack of trust in his good will."

"That's very interesting, but I'm not sure it tells us much about Elsie's state of mind," said Dan. "Can you think of anything else?"

"Just little things. Sometimes she complained about Clayton's computer collection. She said every time Radio Shack brings out a new model of the Trash-80, Clayton has to have it. She said Clayton is just an overgrown kid. 'Course she said the same thing about me, so it doesn't mean too much. Probably just her outlook on men in general."

Kit finished his coffee and was getting up to leave when the man himself came in and ordered a coffee to go.

"That doesn't look like your work suit," said Dan.

"Nope," said Clayton, "it's my funeral suit."

"Didn't know anybody had died," said Phil.

"Not in Pemberton," said Clayton. "Old Bill Graves down in Bruce Mines. Haven't seen much of Bill since he went into the Manor down at Thessalon, but he's as close as I ever had to a father. Got my first job from him when I was ten and worked for him off and on through my teens."

"Guess we're heading for the same place," said Kit. "I have to pick up George Hagen at the Castle and take him down to Bruce Mines."

"Bill Graves had a farm just out of town, didn't he?" said Phil.

"Yes. Don't know what will happen to it now. The folks on the next farm to the east started taking off the hay when Bill sold his milk quota, but the place hasn't been farmed properly in ten years. He's got a niece in Thessalon and a nephew at the plant up in the Soo and some others further away. I don't think any of them has any interest." Clayton picked up his coffee and both he and Kit hurried out.

"A lot of farms along the North Shore are being turned to pasture or not being used at all," said Dan after they left. "Is the land running out or is it just that people don't want to farm?"

"If land is going to run out, it does it in about five years," said Phil. "Folks been farming on the North Shore for a hundred years, so it's got to be something else. I've got to get back to work, but here's the man will give you the real dope about farming."

Jake Harden was just coming in. "I wanted to get here before you left," he said to Phil, "but I had a sick calf and had to wait for the vet. Guess I'll have to settle for Dan."

"Shouldn't you be on the land?" asked Phil. "It's a warm sunny day out there."

"Yes, it is," said Jake, "and yes I should. But after all the rain we had last week, the fields are still a little too wet. Maybe tomorrow if this weather holds up."

Jake ordered a coffee, sat down opposite Dan and handed him a typewritten sheet. "Here's a 'Jay's Nest' column that hasn't gone to press. Tell me what you think.

Dealer: East
Neither Vul.

North (Jake)
♠ A 10 9 4
♡ 5 3
◇ Q 10 9 3
♣ Q 10 2

West (Barry)
♠ 5 2
♡ K 6 4 2
◇ K J 5
♣ K 8 5 4

East (Kevin)
♠ J 7 3
♡ 10 8
◇ A 7 4 2
♣ J 9 6 3

South (Jay)
♠ K Q 8 6
♡ A Q J 9 7
◇ 8 6
♣ A 7

West	North	East	South
		1♡!	pass
1NT	pass	2◇	2♡
dbl	pass	3♣	pass
pass	3◇	pass	3NT
all pass			

Opening lead: ♣4

When Kevin and Barry discovered psyches, they jumped in with both feet. A psyche is a lie, but it's legal at bridge. Which makes the psyche an irresistible outlet for the larceny in the souls of honest young men. Kevin on my right opened one heart with the East hand for no good reason that I can see except that it was his turn to bid. This shut me up good and proper. Here I was preparing to make a Flannery bid, even though I had an extra point, but after the heart bid there was nothing I could do so I passed. Barry on my left bid a forcing notrump and Kevin bid two diamonds. I was afraid that if I passed the bidding might die right there, so I took the bull by the horns and bid two hearts. Barry on my left wasn't sure what to make of that, so just in case his partner really had his heart bid, he doubled to show his raise. My partner was Jake, the only expert in the club I get to play with regularly. I played rubber bridge with him when he was just a tadpole. Even though he's now much better than me, he still asks me to play. He says it keeps him honest, whatever that means.

After I bid two hearts, Jake had things pretty much figured out, so he was happy to have me play there even though I was doubled. Then Kevin pulled to three clubs. When this came back to Jake, he temporized — that's the way he talks now — with a cuebid of three diamonds. I didn't know what to do, so I bid three notrump. It was now clear that Kevin had psyched (even I could figure that out). But there was no rule that said he couldn't have the king of hearts, so after a club to the ten, jack and my ace, I crossed to the ace of spades and played a heart to my queen. Barry won and could have held me to nine tricks by cashing out, but he had no idea what his partner held. Instead, he just played king and another club, which allowed me to make an overtrick.

Holding me to my game would have been an average. Even though four spades is a better spot, some people didn't get to game and two pairs who were in four spades didn't make it. Of the others in four spades, only one made an overtrick (Jake said they must have gotten a heart lead) so we had a second top. I was going to ask to see the psycher's hand, but Jake was more interested in his partner's hand. When it was spread out, it was clear that he had a limit raise in hearts.

Since they were playing that a jump raise in hearts would be a limit raise, Jake asked why he had not bid it.

"Well, I had a feeling about it."

"What do you suppose gave you that feeling?" asked Jake, and suddenly I realized where he was going. Barry and Kevin, who are bright young men, figured it out too.

"Oh, it wasn't anything in the way my partner bid," said Barry.

"How can you be sure?" asked Jake, "Jay's pass over the one-heart bid was so smooth that it had me fooled. One of the problems with psyches is that you are only allowed to figure them out from the auction. In particular, you are not allowed to use your partner's body language or voice inflection.

"If you start using table feel, it's pretty hard to be sure that feeling didn't come from your partner."

"It's a good thing you handled that one," I said to Jake after they left. "I probably would have accused them of cheating. Do you think you convinced them to quit psyching?"

"Not a chance. The confidence of young men is such that they will be sure they can psyche without getting into moral problems. They will stop, eventually, when they run into bidding problems from holding back or just not believing each other."

Or when they once too often keep us out of our normal contract and get a bottom as a result.

"It has its moments," said Dan when he finished reading the column, "but it's more like a sermon than a bridge column."

"Do you think she should send it in?"

"I don't know. How do you think the boys will take it?"

"That's what I'm worried about," said Jake. "Katie too. It's one thing for me to tell them, in private, to be careful. It's quite another for Katie to tell all of Pemberton they're walking the fine line between devil-may-care bridge and cheating."

"Right. We don't want to turn off the kids by forbidding them to psyche. Or by accusing them of cheating. At the same time, if they start fielding one another's psyches, even in complete innocence, we've got to let them know they're in cheating territory. For one thing, if we turn a blind eye at the club, the first time they go to a tournament they'll get called on it, probably by someone who's pissed off and uses the "C" word. I think, for now, your little lecture is enough."

"Good. I just wanted to hear somebody else say it. I'll tell Katie to put it aside. Maybe leave it for her collected works." Jake paused briefly. "What did you want to know about farming? Have you finally decided to do something useful with your life?"

"Just before you came in, Clayton came through on his way to a funeral in Bruce Mines."

"Bill Graves," said Jake.

"Clayton did chores for him when he was a kid. Anyway, there's nobody to take over the farm and I was wondering why there are so many abandoned farms up and down the North Shore."

"Standard of living," said Jake, who had given this question some thought. "The average farmer makes a piss-poor living for the amount of work he puts into it. In my great-grandfather's day, it was much better, relatively speaking. Enough better that the oldest son would lay claim to the family farm and younger sons had to find a different career or buy their own farm."

"What was so different then?"

"Lots of things, I guess. But mainly it was the horses. All the horses in lumber camps needed hay, oats, and straw. In the Soo, there were livery stables where you could rent a horse and there were horses pulling taxis, bakers' and butchers' vans, and all of the dairies had horses for their milk wagons. All those city horses and lumber camp horses needed to be fed. Hay and oats were the gasoline of the time and farmers supplied it. After the internal combustion engine took over, farmers still produced food for people, but they no longer supplied fuel for the main means of transportation."

"So it has nothing to do with us being too far north?"

"That's part of it. Down south they can double crop and grow things like soybeans. On the other hand, farmers have been proving for the past hundred years you can grow crops and raise livestock here. And land is cheaper here, so it's easier to get a start."

"It seems to me," said Dan, "That when Connie and I came to Pemberton, the horses were long gone, except for a few throwbacks like old Lester Gordon, but farmers were still doing okay."

"You're right. Gasoline power didn't destroy farming. It just made it into a borderline situation. The kicker is that the price of food, relative to an average salary, just keeps going down. Eighty years ago, a quart of milk cost ten cents and a dozen eggs cost fifteen cents. That probably sounds like the good old days from your point of view. But $300 was a good yearly wage. In other words, everything should be multiplied by a hundred. If you were paying ten dollars for a quart of milk and fifteen dollars for a dozen eggs, I'd be making a pretty good living. As it is, I've got to be careful or I can spend more growing a crop than I get out of it."

Jake stopped a moment to let that sink in and then continued.

"If you just want to get by, the farm is still not a bad place to do it. On a mixed farm with a wood lot, you can be almost self-sufficient. So if you sell a little milk, eggs, pork and beef, even at present prices, you can survive. There's not many people willing to accept a subsistence sort of life, so the mixed farm is disappearing. If you want to have the same standard of living on the farm as a guy working in the Soo at the steel plant, you have to expand, and specialize, and go into debt for equipment to make you more efficient... and work your butt off. If you're lucky, you'll do well. Some farmers aren't lucky."

"Even so," said Dan, "I can't help but feel that surviving on a small farm in Northern Ontario would be better than being homeless in Toronto. With all the empty space we have here, there shouldn't be people freezing on the streets of Toronto."

"Starting up a farm, even a small one, takes a big investment," said Jake." Homeless people have no way of getting started. And somebody with the kind of nest egg it takes to get started in farming isn't thinking his only two options are to farm in Northern Ontario or to be homeless in Toronto.

"Besides," continued Jake, "people aren't born knowing how to farm. If you gave a homeless guy a start and he really applied himself and worked hard, he'd still be broke again in a couple of years. Years ago, just about every farm had a hired man. If you wanted to farm you could do your apprenticeship by hiring on somewhere. Now, with all the equipment, very few of the small-to-medium-sized farms have hired hands, so it's harder to get on-the-job training.

"Not only did the internal combustion engine eliminate a source of income for the farmer," Jake summed up as he got up to leave, "it also eliminated the need for a lot of farmer apprentices."

* * * * *

Angie's Kevin was working at the Brickworks for the summer. Given names have always gone in and out of style. Television has made this tendency even more pronounced. In the early 1960's in Pemberton, seventeen baby boys were named Kevin. One of these Kevins played bridge. Two other Kevins were working that summer at the Brickworks. Angie's Kevin was just coming out of the lunch room when Phil got back from his lunch break.

"Got a minute?" said Phil.

It took more than a minute. Kevin had clear memories of the day Elsie died which, under pressure from Angie, he had kept them to himself. He seemed relieved to be asked about it. The sound of the smoke alarm had not been loud when they first heard it back at the pond, but it had been unmistakable.

Phil had gone more than a month without smoking, but he had not lost the desire to light up. Whenever somebody said 'smoke,' no matter what the context, Phil would reach for the pack that was no longer in his breast pocket. This conditioned reflex was getting weaker but had not gone away. Today the word had more punch than usual. Phil wondered if it was his addiction making a last ditch attempt to turn Phil back into a smoker or if there was something about the smoke alarm and its connection with Elsie's death that was making him uncomfortable.

Kevin said, "When we got to the edge of the canyon, the alarm was quite loud but sort of fuzzy around the edges as though the sound was coming through a fog."

"That's odd," said Phil. "Have you ever heard a smoke alarm, or for that matter, any kind of alarm, sound like that?"

Kevin was unable to be more specific.

They didn't hear the train until it came into sight. Kevin assumed they didn't hear it sooner because there was too much going on. They were panting by the time they reached the edge of the canyon. The smoke alarm was howling and there was a lady charging across the trestle. Phil had some trouble accepting this as an explanation for not hearing the train. When part of the excitement is a lady running across a railway bridge, the noise of a train would surely get your attention.

If the train had been audible, he thought, then Kevin would have noticed. Elsie would have been listening for the train, so presumably she didn't hear it either. That business about putting your head to the track would be just to put Clayton's mind at ease. She probably knew exactly how long you could hear the train before it appeared and figured to be able to make it. No need to speculate, though. He could go out there some weekend and clock the train from the time he heard it to the time it appeared. Perhaps with Dan. No, he thought, Dan has closed the book on this business until something more substantial than vague suspicions comes along. Phil would have nothing solid until he knew for certain that the train was usually audible long before it reached the bridge. Phil had a gut feeling that if Clayton was involved in Elsie's jump in any way, then the smoke alarm was the key. But maybe his gut was just reacting to the fact that every time he heard 'smoke alarm' the addiction center in his brain sent a message down to his gut saying, 'Did you hear that? The word was smoke. I repeat: smoke, smoke, smoke.'

C H A P T E R

Clayton arrived at Grant's funeral home in Bruce Mines in time to offer condolences to nieces and nephews. Since Bill had never married and had outlived his sisters, there was no close family. As the service began, Clayton thought back to his eighteenth birthday when he had learned that his mother had more to do with him getting work on the Grave's farm than he had previously realized.

When Clayton was ten, his mother arranged with Bill Graves, who had a farm on the edge of town, to hire Clayton to do light chores, such as bringing in the cows at milking time. What Clayton didn't know at the time was that his mother paid money to Bill Graves, which was in turn paid to him each week. She wanted Clayton to do something for his allowance. Bill Graves suspected that what Clarissa really wanted was a male presence in Clayton's life. This was an astute observation on Bill's part, but he didn't know that Clarissa also hoped that when Clayton was old enough to do real paying jobs on the farm, at plowing, cultivating, seeding and harvest time, Clayton would be the natural choice.

There was something else Clayton learned on his eighteenth birthday — something that made the devious business with Bill Graves pale in comparison. Once in a while an adopted child doesn't learn about being adopted until he or she becomes an adult. Not so with Clayton. It seemed to him that as far back as he could remember he had known he was adopted. The shock for him, on his eighteenth birthday, was learning that his adoptive mother was actually his birth mother.

She told Clayton when he turned eighteen. The whole story came out in bits and pieces over the next few years. Clarissa Carmichael was born and raised in Sault Ste Marie, went to Normal School in Ottawa and got her first teaching post in Bruce Mines. Her parents were among the first Northern Ontario snowbirds. In the winter of 1937, Clarissa, by putting in a lot of extra hours on the Christmas concert, was able to arrange an extra week off from school before Christmas to spend the holiday with her parents in Florida.

The Carmichael Florida home was in a town where circus people spent the winter. The normally prim Clarissa, liberated by being in a strange country, had a brief passionate affair with a young midway barker. Six weeks later, Clarissa realized that she had more than bittersweet memories from her Florida fling. Clarissa was in despair for a full week.

Then she started to revive. Though her case seemed hopeless at first, Clarissa was a survivor. She saw a way out of her predicament and plotted a campaign. The first step was to enlist the help of childhood friend Janet Reese, who was nursing in Toronto. Clarissa composed letters, which she mailed to Janet. Janet promptly mailed them back to her from Toronto. The first letter purported to be from Clarissa's estranged half-sister, Liza, who was newly married and already with child. This letter and later ones were shared with Clarissa's landlady, Hazel Sharp, which was sufficient to get the word out to the rest of the town.

After a few weeks, Liza wrote to say that the marriage was in trouble and in a few more weeks Liza was on her own. Clarissa resolved to go to Toronto to be with Liza as soon as school was out. In the meantime, she started wearing bulky clothes from time to time so that no one would become suspicious when she had to wear them all the time.

By the end of the term, she had put on a few pounds and a few observant ladies were speculating, but no one actually disbelieved her story. Clarissa's letters from Toronto that summer revealed that Liza was having a difficult pregnancy and no one was surprised when she died in childbirth. The baby boy was healthy and Clarissa remained in Toronto an extra week to arrange an adoption.

In that time, she changed her mind and decided to 'adopt' the child herself. For most of the summer, she really had intended to give her baby up for adoption. But in the last month of her pregnancy she started to imagine scenarios where she kept her baby.

She called Hazel, who was very accommodating and offered to look after the baby while Clarissa was at school. In fact, Hazel was even willing to officially adopt the child. Party phone lines being what they were, this news was known to the whole town before Hazel had a chance to tell anybody.

Female teachers always stopped teaching as soon as they got married and had children. Clarissa wasn't married and while the members of the board thought they knew what was going on, Clarissa was a good teacher, popular with both staff and students, so they decided not to make an issue of it. Single parents were uncommon when Clayton arrived in Bruce Mines. That changed over the next few years as young men went off to the war, leaving pregnant wives behind them to cope on their own. Some of those young men never came back.

The first time Clayton went with Bill Graves to fetch the cows, he discovered it was not always necessary to go beyond the herd in order to drive them up to the barn. As soon as they were close to the cows, Bill began to shout, "Co-boss, co-boss."

"Why do you say co-boss?" asked Clayton.

"I dunno, it's just how we always call 'em. Don't s'pose it matters much what you say. You're just getting their attention. But it's what we shout, so it's what they're used to. Generally at milking time, their udders are starting to get uncomfortable so all you have to do is remind them it's time and they start for the barn. Not all the time though. Sometimes they just plain ignore you. Don't know why. Then you got to get down behind them and drive them up."

"How come you don't have a dog to help drive them?"

"Could do. Used to have a collie, old Danny, that was pretty good. But even a good dog gets excited if a cow don't mind. The last thing you want is a dog putting the run on a cow with a bag full of milk. She might hurt herself and even if she don't, she won't let all her milk down. So it hurts production. You heard about contented cows? That's no bullshit. Contented cows give more milk."

Clayton liked driving in the cows, even though it bugged him that they didn't pay attention to his "Co-boss, co-boss." What he did discover was that if he drove up the first group of cows he came to and shouted at the rest, then they would come too. This became his standard method for bringing in the cows. In fact, he found, after a while, that even if he just drove the first cow he came to, the rest would follow.

One day, the closest cow was the one called June. The rest of the herd was somewhat further down the pasture, but he gave them a shout and drove June up to the barn.

When he got there, Bill asked, "Where's the rest of them?"

Clayton hadn't been paying any attention to what was happening, or wasn't happening, behind him. "They always come," he said, "even when I just drive up the first one." He had come to think of his job as driving up one cow. If the rest didn't follow, that wasn't his problem.

"Guess you never drove up June before, eh? Have you ever noticed she don't mix much with the other cows. Cows got a herding instinct. That's why you can cut out a few, or even one, and the rest will follow. But in every herd there's a few outsiders. They kind of hang around the edge of the herd and if they wander off the other cows don't seem to take notice.

"Kind of like people that way," continued Bill. "Take Sally Hopper, that's president of the Women's Institute. If you was to put a bee in her bonnet about making quilts, it wouldn't be long before every woman in town was making quilts. On the other hand, it wouldn't matter what you got Faith Jones down to the library to do. The whole town would know what she was doing, but there wouldn't be anybody following her lead."

Clayton had noticed that June the cow was always pretty much off by herself, never very far from the herd but never in the center of it either. He just hadn't given this any thought. Bill Graves' observations about June and the analogy to the people of the town came as something of a revelation. He didn't pursue this at the time, however, because he had to go back down to the pasture and drive up the rest of the herd, resenting the cows and Bill Graves.

The end of the funeral ceremony brought Clayton back into the present. The mourners walked from the church to the graveyard. After a short ceremony there, Clayton made the rounds, renewing old acquaintances and introducing himself to those he did not know. He was ensuring he would be a familiar face. This was the sort of thing he used to do before he retired and he did it now instinctively. Also, in this instance, he was revisiting his past.

He felt nostalgic and was in no hurry to leave.

Clayton had a clear visual memory of June the cow. Bill Graves' observation about her was a life lesson that struck a particularly responsive cord. At first the comparison of cows with people was just amusing. But Clayton started paying more attention to town society and was surprised to discover there really were similarities between humans and his herd of cows. He took a particular interest in outsiders. Not that he had personal experience of being an outsider — he was gregarious and got along with his classmates. But being adopted had set him a little apart. He felt instinctively that even though outsiders had less need to belong and followed their own inner light, they had, nevertheless, chosen a lonely path and a little bit of human warmth would make a big impression. As a future salesman, he felt he ought to be able to reach such people. Johnny Bates, in his class, was an outsider. Johnny went his own way and seemed not to care when he was not included in activities. Clayton, in experimental mode, decided to befriend Johnny to see if he was a loner because he wanted to be or because he was usually ignored. Johnny was pathetically grateful for the attention.

Clayton felt he had learned something important about human (and cow) nature. A practical application of this lesson came a few years later. Karen Farmer made a meager living painting local scenes on driftwood, birch bark, and flat rocks, which were then sold to tourists at gift shops in Bruce Mines and Thessalon. She was a brusque independent young woman, and when Clayton just happened (by design) to be checking out behind her at the general store and offered to help carry her groceries, she informed him she was quite capable of carrying her own groceries thank you. Clayton felt a small part of his world crumble. He had been waiting for such an opportunity for several weeks and was quite sure of her reaction. It was not this.

Karen was not overtly feminine — she often wore men's clothes and made no effort to make herself attractive to the opposite sex. She was, nevertheless, sufficiently attractive that in ordinary times she would have had a boyfriend. In this time after the war, there were more women of her age in Bruce Mines than men. There were no men in her life and she didn't mix much with the women of the town. She was an outsider like June the cow and Clayton had assumed she would be quite pleased to be befriended by him.

He found out he had it right, in the main. It's just that grown women were more complex than cows and young boys. A few days later, Clarissa got a call asking if Clayton would be interested in making a little money doing yard work — Karen needed help moving rocks for a garden she was making in her side yard. Clayton accepted. It was warm work and Clayton removed his shirt, revealing a lean tanned torso, well muscled from his work on the farm. Clayton was soon glistening with sweat. Karen had changed into a loose short-sleeved cotton blouse and was working alongside him. Clayton became aware of a growing sexual tension, which he thought was all in his own head. He was just fifteen and she must have been in her late twenties. As he and Karen leaned over to lift a large rock, he found himself looking down her blouse at full, beautiful breasts. He somehow managed to lift his end of the rock and when it was in place, Karen put her bare arm over his bare shoulders and said, "Well done." His shoulder touched the side of her breast. Involuntarily, he pressed against her. "Let's go inside," she said.

Karen became Clayton's first lover and he maintained a casual relationship with her through his teen years. There was affection, but no great love on either side, and it wasn't clear who was taking advantage of whom.

Clayton continued to work on the farm until he finished high school. Clarissa had been right that fetching the cows would give Clayton an inside track for the real work of the farm. Clayton loved the tractor and was always ready for any task which involved driving. He took great pride in making clean square turns when cutting hay and grain. Both the hay mower and the grain binder were originally horse drawn machines on which the draw bar was shortened so they could be pulled by the tractor.

An unusual feature of tractors was that there were separate brake pedals for the rear left and right wheels, and no brake at all for the front wheels. To have the mower make a clean right-angle turn, it was necessary to time the turn precisely. As the sickle bar cleared the end of the row, he would yank the steering wheel full right while stepping hard on the right rear brake to bring that wheel of the tractor to a full stop. The inner wheel of the mower would come to a standstill and the sickle bar would arc backwards until the tractor had turned ninety degrees. Then he would straighten the steering wheel and take his foot off the brake. The tractor and mower would surge forward, cutting a full swath across the end of the field.

The sign of sloppy turns was a jagged broken line of uncut stalks of grain or hay running in from the corners of the field toward the center. When they were out driving in their new second-hand car on Sunday afternoons, Clayton would point out to Clarissa his own clean fields and the less than perfect ones of some of the neighbors.

Bill Graves was completely satisfied with the work that Clayton did on the tractor. For physical chores, like stooking sheaves of grain and piling bales of hay, Clayton's work was not as precise. On balance, however, Clayton's work was good enough that he had a job on the farm during the busy summer season for as long as he wanted it.

Clayton's relationship with Karen continued for several years. In order to justify his visits in the eyes of the town, Karen started to do more painting on canvas and used Clayton as a model for figures in Bruce Mines landscapes. This didn't stop the town gossips from talking: "Mark my words, there's more going on there than meets the eye." Nevertheless, even those who professed to have no doubt about the immoral goings on would have been startled to discover their worst suspicions were, in fact, justified. For the gossips never totally believed what they maintained for certain fact.

The affair ended when Karen abruptly left town in the spring of 1955. She had a friend who was acting in the big tent in Stratford and they needed a scene and prop painter. Karen had two days to make up her mind. It took her two minutes. Clayton and Karen both promised to write but neither ever did.

Not all of Clayton's life's lessons came as epiphanies. Clayton learned a lesson from his mother that was much more important, though neither of them was aware of teaching or learning. Clarissa had a standard Northern Ontario Christian outlook on life. She knew, among other things, that honesty was good and lying was bad. Where Clarissa digressed from the standard, perhaps just a little, was that she allowed herself some degree of flexibility when it came to telling the truth. She exempted herself from truth-telling when a lie promoted the greater good.

In connection with Clayton's ancestry, Clarissa told countless lies and deceived a whole town and several townships without any twinge of conscience. It hadn't even occurred to her that there might be a moral problem with the deception she practiced in connection with Clayton's job with Bill Graves. Her conscience was not quite so clear when she failed to declare U.S. purchases at Customs, but she had trouble paying twice for things just because she'd bought them across the border.

The net effect was that Clayton learned from his mother, through example, that it was okay to lie and deceive if it was for the greater good. This was a principle which neither of them ever put into words — Clayton learned it from the way Clarissa acted and from how she justified small transgressions. The difference between Clayton and his mother was that she had a strongly developed moral sense. While her own interests sometimes bent her vision of the greater good, she would never have lied to hurt others and she sometimes even told the truth when it would have been easier to lie. This allowed her to be comfortable in the belief that she was basically an honest person.

Clayton did not have as strong a sense of what was right, though he had a moral upbringing that was very similar to his mother's. He went to Sunday School at the United Church Hall and learned about right and wrong. The difference between Clayton and his mother was that what he learned at Sunday School was a code he expected others to follow (he could be quite indignant about the transgressions of others) and which he avoided being seen to break himself. For his own part, the Sunday School lessons worked poorly as a set of abstract principles to guide his actions in life.

Not that he was bad. He had personal charm and was generally liked by adults and children, even those who found him a tad manipulative. It was just that the guiding principle in his life was a self-interest that was completely self-centered. Clayton had learned from his mother (without anything actually being said) that the principles he learned in Sunday School only applied if they did not conflict with the greater good. For Clayton, there was never any conflict between the greater good and his own welfare.

C H A P T E R

During the second week of May, Kit, Clayton, Fran, Rose, Phil and Dan went up to the Soo in Kit's van for the regular Thursday night bridge game. Playing in the Soo was not a new experience for any of them. Individually, they dropped in on one of the club games from time to time when they happened to be in the Soo during the day; and they played regularly in sectional and regional tournaments in the Soo.

The best players in the district of Algoma were quite well known to each other from meeting at tournaments and at each other's clubs. On the other hand, there were always club players who never strayed far from home. Pemberton had competent players who played lots of rubber bridge and sometimes played duplicate bridge, but only at the Pemberton club. These players could surprise visitors to the

Pemberton club because outsiders tended to assume that unknown players were not very good. And of course, all players, good and bad, had quirks and propensities that those who played regularly against them got to know. Home players always had a slight edge over visitors of similar ability because the home players knew the field.

The Pemberton group would have to play quite a few games in the Soo before they could compete on a level playing field with the best Soo players. Despite this handicap, Fran and Rose had a big game and came first North-South. Phil and Dan were third East-West. Kit and Clayton finished below average, having been fixed by some of the weaker Soo players and by an unusual pair playing an unusual deal.

Kit took a slip of paper out of his breast pocket and handed it to Fran. "This is how our evening went."

N-S Vul.

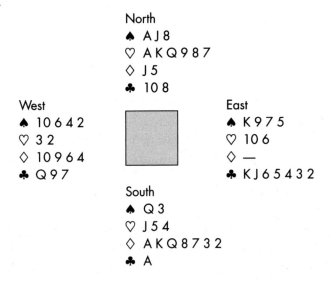

North
♠ A J 8
♡ A K Q 9 8 7
♢ J 5
♣ 10 8

West
♠ 10 6 4 2
♡ 3 2
♢ 10 9 6 4
♣ Q 9 7

East
♠ K 9 7 5
♡ 10 6
♢ —
♣ K J 6 5 4 3 2

South
♠ Q 3
♡ J 5 4
♢ A K Q 8 7 3 2
♣ A

"Oh yes," said Fran. "This is the one where North has six hearts headed by the top three honors and South has seven diamonds headed by the top three honors. Not our best effort. It makes fifteen tricks in notrump or either red suit. We stopped in six notrump. Fortunately for us there was just one pair that bid the grand. So we lucked out, tied for second top with two other pairs who played the slam in notrump rather than hearts."

"The grand," said Kit, "was bid by those two brothers that show up at our club every few years. One of them plays kitchen bridge. The other one thinks he's a hotshot."

"That would be Bill and Joe Burnside," said Rose. "Joe lives in Echo Bay which puts him halfway between our club and the Soo clubs. He only plays duplicate when his brother comes to visit. Bill is a regular duplicate player. Probably a life master."

"How did your auction go?" said Dan.

Kit had never been very good at reviewing auctions. Clayton was somewhat better, but he was quiet this evening and seemed to be having trouble concentrating on the subject at hand. Between the two of them, the following picture emerged.

Kit was East and had the first bid. Some players would preempt with his hand but with a void and a four-card major he passed. The hotshot opened one diamond. His brother sat for an eternity and then bid three hearts.

"Splinter?" Kit asked.

"We don't play splinters," said Hotshot.

"What is it then?"

"We have no agreement but I'd be happy to give you my best guess if you want."

"That would certainly help your partner," said Clayton.

"Go grab a coffee," said Hotshot to his brother, who started to say he didn't want a coffee, then got up and left.

The explanation was that they do play jump shifts strong and Hotshot's best guess was that a double jump would be a strong hand with a strong suit. Kit bid four clubs and Hotshot bid seven hearts.

"You already know what we got for that," said Kit.

"Your just deserts, for bidding four clubs," said Rose, who thought that Bill Burnside was a nice man and did not deserve to be called Hotshot.

"How do you figure? We weren't vulnerable, after all,"

"You knew they were flying by the seat of their pants and Bill Burnside was going to have to guess at how high to go. So why tell him that none of his partner's values for the double jump shift were wasted in clubs?"

"Good point," said Fran. "Though I'm in no position to criticize. We don't have that double jump shift in our bag of tricks, but I could have, and should have, bid two hearts over Rose's one-diamond opener. Then, getting to one of the grands is trivial. Phil and Dan, you were East-West. How did it go at your table?"

"Phil opened three clubs with Kit's hand," said Dan.

"Disciplined Phil? Of course he would," said Kit.

"South overcalled three diamonds," continued Dan. "I took a look at the vulnerability — they were vul, we weren't — and then thought 'what would Phil bid if he was looking at my cards opposite a three club preempt?' — forgetting for the moment that if I held Phil's cards I might not have opened three clubs. My way was clear — I bid six clubs. That was doubled. Down four. Minus 800 was well above average."

Clayton had very little to say about any of the deals they discussed. Rose finally turned to him and asked, "What's the matter Clayton, are you letting one bad game get you down?".

"The game didn't help," said Clayton. "But this was my second trip to the Soo today. I went up this morning see my lawyer. Elsie's will was a little vague on a couple of points and I thought the executor made the wrong interpretation. I went to a lawyer in the Soo who specializes in estate law and he agreed." He frowned. "My court date has been postponed twice, so it's still not resolved. I figure about five minutes in court should do it. But it's been close to a year and still no decision. Pisses me off."

Nobody said anything. Kit thought the will was clear and the executor's interpretation correct. Then again, he had so little knowledge of estate law that he didn't have an opinion about whether there were grounds for a challenge. If they had done better at the table, he might have argued anyway. As it was, he let it pass.

* * * * *

Bad luck runs in streaks. Kit was still being dogged by it through the next game in Pemberton. When he arrived at the Cornerstone after the game on Tuesday night, Kit, as usual, ignored the discussion already in progress and tossed a diagram into the middle of the table. "Can somebody tell me what right the Doc has getting smart all of a sudden?"

Dealer: East
Neither Vul.

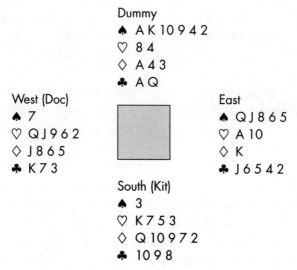

Dummy
♠ A K 10 9 4 2
♡ 8 4
◇ A 4 3
♣ A Q

West (Doc)
♠ 7
♡ Q J 9 6 2
◇ J 8 6 5
♣ K 7 3

East
♠ Q J 8 6 5
♡ A 10
◇ K
♣ J 6 5 4 2

South (Kit)
♠ 3
♡ K 7 5 3
◇ Q 10 9 7 2
♣ 10 9 8

West	North	East	South
		pass	pass
2♡	dbl	pass	3◇
pass	3♠	pass	3NT
all pass			

"The opening lead is the heart queen (a small heart would have worked better for the defense). RHO wins with the ace and plays back the heart ten. You let it hold and RHO now switches to a club to dummy's queen. You think about a low diamond to your nine, hoping it forces the king. But this would give LHO a chance to score a stiff jack. And besides, if the king rather than the jack is stiff on your left, you can drop it by playing the ace and then bring in the diamonds without a loser by finessing twice against the jack. So you play the ace, dropping the king, but on your right rather than on your left. Now what?"

"Let's see," said Phil, "the club finesse is on, the diamond king drops stiff and you're still two tricks short of game. I hope we're not looking for overtricks here."

"Actually, now that you've dropped the king of diamonds, you're gin," said Mac. "Just force out the diamond jack and you've got two spades, a heart, four diamonds and two clubs for nine tricks. And, with just twenty-two points between the two hands, nobody in their right mind is going to be in this contract, so you've got a top. Where's the problem?"

"The problem," said Kit, "is that if you play queen and another diamond to LHO's jack, then the Doc on your left will just put you back in dummy with a club and you'll never get back to your heart trick and the two diamond tricks you just set up."

"Right," said Phil, "so what you have to do is cash your spade and club tricks to strip Doc and hope he doesn't unblock the club king. When he wins his diamond jack, he can cash his club king if he wants, but then he'll have to come back to you with a red card."

"Exactly," said Kit, "once Doc shows out of spades, I know the exact distribution of both concealed hands. And since the club king would have given RHO an opening bid, I know Doc has it. But who would have thought he was up to playing it under the ace and keeping the three to get over to his partner's jack."

"Maybe you shouldn't have cashed the spades first," said Mac. "By the time you played the club ace, the writing was on the wall."

"Of course I played the spades first," said Kit. "If one of the spade honors comes down doubleton, then I make an overtrick by continuing spades and I don't have to worry about what Doc does in diamonds."

Dan, Fran and Rose had been uncharacteristically silent. Finally, Dan said, "Give Doc credit for unblocking the king. I don't think he would have done it a few months ago, but ever since he avoided Clayton's pseudo endplay, he's been concentrating a little more and he's picked his game up a notch. Even so, you could have made it. Fran and I had the same auction and she made it."

"No way," said Kit. "Unless the defense gets friendly. Who were you playing against?"

"Rose held the Doc's cards," said Dan. "Actually, that's where Fran had an advantage over you. The only thing Rose likes better than ducking is unblocking, so Fran didn't waste time thinking about a line that would work only if Rose didn't unblock."

"After the diamond king drops," continued Dan, "this is very nearly a double-dummy problem. Rose is known to have started with nine red cards, so must have exactly four black cards. Fran came up with a line of play which succeeds against any four black cards."

Dan waited while the other's studied the diagram for a way to make against best defense. Even double-dummy, this hand was no cinch.

After a few minutes Mac spoke up, "I don't see anything better than Kit and Phil's line." Mac was one of the few good players who would admit to not seeing something. The rest would have studied the diagram for another hour before admitting they didn't see a better line.

Dan continued, "The first thing Fran did was to play a diamond to her ten. If Rose wins, then Fran still has a diamond in dummy for communication to run the diamonds and make her contract. So Rose has to duck. I'm not sure the Doc would have been up to ducking in that position." Dan couldn't resist letting Kit know his contract was there for the taking by giving Doc a chance to make this mistake rather than depending on him not to see the unblocking play.

"Ducking was routine for Rose of course. Playing to the ten gives Rose a chance to make a mistake, but it is also a necessary play — after taking that trick with the diamond ten, Fran has taken three tricks and with five more to come in high cards, she just needs one more trick for her game. Taking the diamond ten sets up the squeeze. You've heard of losing a trick to rectify the count? Well this is a case of winning a trick with a losing card in order to rectify the count... even though, by usual counting methods, the count is still two tricks short of being rectified. Fran can now endplay Stan and at the same time squeeze Rose in three suits. Fran played a spade to dummy's ace and king, leading to this position:

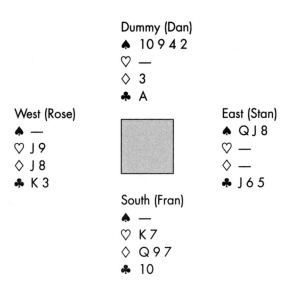

Dummy (Dan)
♠ 10 9 4 2
♡ —
♢ 3
♣ A

West (Rose)
♠ —
♡ J 9
♢ J 8
♣ K 3

East (Stan)
♠ Q J 8
♡ —
♢ —
♣ J 6 5

South (Fran)
♠ —
♡ K 7
♢ Q 9 7
♣ 10

"Fran now called for the spade ten from dummy and pitched her last club. The club ten was her only entry to the dummy, but she knows Stan has to put her back there, so she doesn't need it and pitching the club allows her to keep all her red cards until Rose commits herself. Look at what this does to Rose. Since Fran has the heart seven as a threat in hearts and the nine and seven of diamonds as a two-trick threat, Rose can't pitch a heart or a diamond without giving up a trick. So she has to pitch a club. Meanwhile, Stan can't afford to duck the spade ten or that will give Fran her ninth trick. So he wins, and he can't continue spades without giving up a trick, so he puts Fran back in dummy with a club. Fran's heart seven has done its job, so it goes on the club. Now she's home free. She can give up the diamond to Rose, who no longer has a little club for an exit card."

This was the hand of the year, but Dan and Fran had agreed to hold off talking about it until Kit arrived. That Kit had come in waving the hand was all the better. "That's as pretty as it gets," continued Dan. "If you wouldn't give up a year of your life to have made that play at the table, then you're not a bridge player."

After accolades for Fran from the whole group, Rose asked, "How about you Fran? Was that hand worth a year of your life?"

"That's just man talk," said Fran. She paused. "A week maybe."

CHAPTER 21

Jake joined Dan and Phil at Mary's Lunch the next day, partway through the noon hour. "Hear I missed a beauty," he said.

"Sure did," said Phil. "How'd you find out?"

"Kit called me. Since he hadn't figured it out, he wanted to give me a chance to miss it too before somebody accidentally told me the best line of play. Very pretty, I must say."

"Did you get it?" asked Phil.

"Not in the five minutes Kit gave me before telling me Fran's line. What I want to know is did Fran see the whole thing right from the start?"

"I wondered the same thing," said Dan. "She said she saw squeeze possibilities as soon as the diamond king dropped stiff, but she also saw she could make the hand if Rose won the second diamond, so she didn't think it completely through until after Rose ducked."

"How did Kit get hold of you?" asked Phil. "You must be plowing and planting most of the time these days."

"You've got that right. Finished discing and raking my big field down by the creek last night at 9:30 p.m. That's why I wasn't out to the game. Started seeding this morning at 4:00 a.m. Got half an hour done before I had to start the chores. Kit knows I generally come in from chores and have breakfast at 7:30, so that's when he called."

"Don't suppose you're here because the seeding's all done?"

"Nope, there's lots left to do. Spent most of the morning planting oats, but a bar on the seed drill broke. It's over at Russell's getting welded. It's just a twenty-minute job but I was second in line. I'll pick it up as soon as I have a bite."

"I've been thinking about your lecture on farming on the North Shore," said Dan. "Where did you get your information on the old days?"

"All over the place," said Jake. "Some of it came from my father's father and from both of my grandmothers. Unfortunately, I just have sketchy memories of what they told me. I didn't write anything down and now they're gone. Since then, I sat down with my mother and taped her telling everything she can remember. Also, when things slack off during the winter for the past three years, I've been visiting some of the old-timers around Pemberton Township and I've been going in to the Castle. Some of them can't remember what they had for breakfast, but they can still tell you stuff from their childhood."

"You must be getting the same story over and over," said Phil.

"I guess that's true, though everybody seems to remember it a little different, even though everybody had to deal with the same problems."

"But why bother?" said Phil, ever the devil's advocate.

"I guess believing history's important is an article of faith," said Jake. "If you don't believe it, it's not easy for me to change your mind. I think it is important and we've got a rare opportunity here. The Indians that lived in this area practiced agriculture of sorts here for years. In fact, they taught the first settlers how to harvest wild hay from the natural meadows. But farming by white settlers started just a little over a hundred years ago and there're a few people still alive that were born during the pioneer days. When historians look at the beginnings of agriculture in the old world, they're looking back six thousand years. All that's left are a few tools and some fossilized seeds as evidence of how it was done. For the beginnings of farming history here in Algoma, we can still talk to folks who lived through it."

Jake continued, "And it wasn't a picnic. We know if Disney was doing a film of pioneer life, it would be cedar rail fences, lamplight, barn raisings and threshing bees."

"What's wrong with showing those things?" asked Phil. "They were an important part of pioneer life."

"Sure, but you've also got to show the loneliness and hardship of long cold winters when the men went off to earn a little cash by working in the bush, leaving the women and children in isolated log cabins where they had to work hard just to eat and keep warm and tend the livestock. That part's not very romantic. It gets forgotten within a generation unless somebody writes it down.

"Something else Disney would gloss over," continued Jake, "is that everybody butchered their own meat. Even in my time, we killed our own chickens. I remember when my dad thought it was time for me to help out. I probably wasn't much more than ten or eleven. I had to grab the chicken's two legs in one hand and hold it so its neck lay on the chopping block. I don't remember whether I was more scared of the chicken or Dad's axe.

"The first time, when the axe came down, the chicken exploded in a frenzy of flapping. I let go. The chicken took off without its head — a chicken's so stupid the head isn't much of a loss. It seemed like that chicken ran around forever, but it must have been just a few seconds. I was frightened and embarrassed. Dad said 'Hell' and turned away and I thought he was shaking in rage. I know now he must have been laughing."

"Are you sure the chicken was actually running and not just flapping its last gasp?" asked Dan.

"There you go," said Jake to Phil. "Dan's talking directly to the guy that was there and he's having a tough time believing. Suppose I'd told you, Phil, and you told Clayton and Clayton told Dan, so he's getting it third hand. He'd assume it was a tall tale and leave it out of his movie. It wasn't even all that unusual — I've talked to lots of other people who've seen the same thing. Of course, if Dan wanted to put it in his movie, he might have to slaughter a whole flock before he got a runner. But that's not the point. The point is that if the actual facts aren't written down and corroborated by lots of witnesses, then much of our history will be lost."

"My problem is how Dan's going to do the headless chicken scene without the animal rights people getting on his case," said Phil.

"My problem," said Jake, "is I've got a field of oats that won't get planted if I sit here all day talking to you guys."

He swallowed the last of his coffee in two gulps and hurried out. Phil did the same.

Dan finished his coffee and was about to leave when Christine came in. She was carrying a cage with a small raccoon. She placed the cage on the chair beside Dan. "I need to talk to you."

"So this is Rocky," said Dan. "Cute little tyke."

Rocky reached a paw through the grid of the cage. Dan broke a piece of crust off his pie and placed it in the little clawed hand. The piece of crust disappeared into Rocky's mouth and the hand came back through the cage.

"Bet you didn't have to teach him how to beg," said Dan.

"I've got a problem," said Christine. "Bertie wants me to move out of my apartment at the Cornerstone."

"Because of this guy?" said Dan, waving his hand toward the cage. Rocky waved back.

"When I first brought Rocky back to the Cornerstone, I was upfront with Bertie. He waffled, saying it wasn't allowed, but that he'd turn a blind eye and see how it worked out. But if Rocky drew attention to himself, then we'd be evicted."

"So you immediately started making moving plans."

"Not exactly, but I did make some inquiries, just in case."

"Anything promising?" asked Dan.

"Corey says you're rattling around in a three-bedroom house."

"Did she also tell you I've been at war with raccoons for the thirty odd years I've been growing a garden?"

"Rocky's a pet. He'd be different."

"Sure he would. What did Rocky do to get Bertie's attention?"

"We were horsing around and all of a sudden he just raced straight up the wall. Got almost to the ceiling and turned and ran down again."

"Left claw marks all the way up and back down again?"

"I'm afraid he did. You can hardly see them and Bertie doesn't know yet, but I can see the writing on the wall, so to speak."

"What makes you think I want claw marks all over my house?"

"Well here's the deal. I want to stay in Pemberton until the end of the summer. Maybe until the leaves turn in the fall. Your house needs redecorating. If you put up Rocky and me for the summer, I'll completely redecorate before I leave this fall."

"How do you know my house needs redecorating?"

"This is Pemberton," said Christine. "There hasn't been any painting or papering done in your house for at least five years before your wife left, or in the ten years since."

"People are going to talk," said Dan.

"You're a doll," said Christine. She leaned over and kissed him on the cheek. "I don't care if people talk. And a young woman and a raccoon in your house will just give you sex appeal. You won't regret it. When can I move in?"

Christine moved in at the end of June. Dan liked having another person around the house, though it didn't change his routine very much because Christine worked long hours away from the house. She went on field trips where she took camping gear and stayed out in the hills, both locally and up on Superior, for up to five days. She always took Rocky with her.

When she was home, Rocky was a rambunctious guest. Sometimes Rocky and Christine would play a game of cards similar to concentration. In concentration, all the cards are spread out face down and then two cards at a time are turned over. The object is to turn over two cards of the same rank. Rocky's game was to turn over cards until the ace of spades appeared. Then Rocky would go berserk, spinning around or racing up and down the walls.

When Dan told Phil about Rocky's card game, Phil advised, "Don't teach him how to bid. We don't want to lose Russell and I'm not sure how he would react if a raccoon played better than him."

Christine was an early riser, sometimes up and out before Dan got up. More often, they had breakfast together. At first, Dan politely put his breakfast reading material aside. As they got more comfortable, he took up his *Bridge Worlds* again. Sometimes he would discuss with Christine a point made in the article he was reading.

One morning this led to a discussion of a hand, from the previous night, which Clayton had played poorly. Almost as soon as the bridge discussion was concluded, Christine asked him if he had been involved in the investigation of Elsie's jump. Even though they had been talking about Clayton, the question came out of left field, as though Christine had been waiting for an opportunity to broach the subject.

"How much do you know about that day?" he asked.

"I was there," she said.

"You mean here in Pemberton."

"No, out on the rocks by Oak Canyon,"

("Jesus," said Phil, when Dan eventually told him. "Did she say what time the brass band went through?")

Dan just looked at her, astounded, and Christine carried on. "I was out there painting when Elsie suddenly appeared. We chatted about blueberries for a while and she looked at my painting and made neutral comments, which made me think she would have preferred something more like a photograph. A car horn honked one long and two short. She said that would be Clayton going into town, so it must be about four o'clock. Then, ten minutes later, we heard the smoke alarm and she dropped her baskets and took off. I covered my painting and closed my paint case and ran to the edge of the canyon. The train was on the trestle shrieking and I got to the edge just in time to see Elsie jump."

"It happened at 4:30," said Dan.

"Yes, I thought later she had the time wrong. Maybe that's why she wasn't expecting a train."

Suddenly Dan made a connection. "That big painting in Mary's Lunch. That's Elsie, isn't it?" (When he next looked at the painting it didn't look nearly so abstract.)

Christine told Dan how she started down into the canyon, fell and twisted her ankle. When she saw men from the train going down, she went back up and retrieved her painting and supplies.

"Did you see Angie and Kevin?" asked Dan.

"Who?"

"Corey's daughter and her boyfriend. They were out there that day."

"I didn't see anything except the train and Elsie falling from the trestle. I still see it just about every day."

* * * * *

Christine left for a day of sketching. Dan poured himself another cup of coffee and replayed the conversation with Christine. There might be an explanation in there of something he had noticed about Christine. When they were gathered at the Cornerstone, Christine was always very alert whenever Clayton was speaking. Clayton was entertaining, but he wasn't Johnny Carson. Dan found it odd.

Did she feel that seeing Elsie fall created a special bond with Elsie's husband? Or did the fact she was the last person to speak with Elsie leave her with a duty to say something to Clayton? On the flip side, maybe the fact that the two honks of the horn turned out to be a signal that told Elsie it was safe to cross the bridge left her with uneasy feelings about Clayton. It certainly bothered Dan.

So how did he feel about this new tidbit of information? Was it time to get the cold file out of storage? *Get a grip*, he said to himself. *You ain't got nuthin'. Give it a rest.*

Dan didn't play a lot of social bridge, but with another bridge player in the house, a game of rubber became a little easier to organize. Phil and Corey came over twice. On the third occasion, Corey had to cancel at the last minute, and Phil got Kit to come instead.

As they came in, Kit said, "The radio is doing a special on reindeer and they just played the Rudolph song. I'm not sure I like hearing Christmas music in July."

"Johnny Fucking Marks," said Dan.

Christine did a double take. She had never heard Dan use the f-word.

"Who is Johnny Marks?"

"He wrote Rudolph the Red-Nosed Fucking Reindeer."

Christine waited. She didn't notice the grins of Phil and Kit and didn't realize until later that they knew what was coming. One of them might, at this point, have prodded Dan to keep him going, but it wasn't necessary. Christine said, "What am I missing?"

This was sufficient to launch Dan. "In 1949, Dasher and Dancer and the rest of Santa's reindeer had dignity and charisma. We didn't know much about them, but what we did know was all good. Then along came Johnny Marks with his Rudolph song. And it wasn't enough to make a hero out of Rudolph. He figured he had to do it on the heads of the other reindeer. So he made them into schoolyard creeps who make fun of the kid with a handicap. Furthermore, they are shallow schoolyard creeps who suddenly love Rudolph as soon as he turns into a hero.

"If all he did was destroy the good reputation of a bunch of reindeer, that would have been bad enough. What's a thousand times worse is he implies, to the children of his audience, that it's okay to make fun of a schoolyard misfit as long as you then love him as soon as he becomes famous. The unspoken message is that if he doesn't become famous, you will, of course, continue to make fun of him." He huffed.

"What sort of a message is that to send to kids? The morals of this country are going to hell in a handbasket and Johnny fucking Marks helped weave the goddamned basket."

Dan's rant sounded sincere but there was something practiced about it. "You've delivered these lines before," said Christine. "I've never heard of Johnny Marks. How did you find out he wrote Rudolph?"

Dan grimaced and then, like an actor stepping out of character, gave her a little smile. "I'd like to say I was so pissed off by the song I made a point of finding out who wrote it. But the fact of the matter is when I first heard Gene Autry singing that song in the Christmas season of 1949, I didn't think twice about it. I might never have really listened to the words if the kid next door to where we lived in Stratford hadn't been named Billy Marks." He rolled his eyes.

"The writer of the song was his uncle or cousin or something. Billy wasn't a bad kid and we chummed around a bit. The one thing that got under my skin about Billy was he sometimes put on airs about his father being a teacher and my father just a mechanic. He only did this when I beat him at something, but it pissed me off just the same. So when he came over after Christmas waving the sheet music to Rudolph and pointing out who wrote it, I was interested but I wasn't all that pleased for him.

"Of course, I didn't immediately launch into a diatribe about what a crummy song it was, but it inclined me to look at it with a critical eye and it seemed to me right away the other reindeer hadn't behaved too well. It was years later I came to realize what a god-awful message the song puts out on the airways every Christmas."

Phil and Kit had started out leaning back in their chairs and were now leaning forward. This was a part of the rant they had not heard before.

"Do you really hate the song," asked Christine, "or do you just enjoy sounding off about it? It's pretty harmless after all."

"I hate it alright. And I don't think it's harmless. Little children start off thinking the world revolves around them, like the sun seems to revolve around the earth. Part of growing up is learning to respect other people, even those less gifted than oneself. Some people remain self-centered and relate to others only as they're useful. Empathy is like a seedling. With good conditions of sun and rain, with good soil and fertilizer, with cultivation and weeding, it will grow into a strong healthy plant. With poor conditions, it may survive, but it will be sickly and unproductive. A song that celebrates bad behavior has a negative effect on the growth of empathy."

"So you think," said Christine, "that criminals aren't born bad. It all depends on how they were raised."

Over the years that Dan had been ranting against the Rudolph song, he had given some thought to the nature or nurture question. He moved into lecture mode. "Jack the Ripper would have been a nasty piece of work no matter how he was raised. Gandhi and Mother Teresa would have been compassionate no matter what. In between there are lots of folks that could go either way. A little over a century ago, the average white person in the Southern USA thought slavery was okay. After slavery was abolished, they still considered black people inferior. Several generations later there may still be some lingering prejudices, but those same average people now feel a little guilty about such feelings and go out of their way not to let them show.

"What happened there on a large scale happens everywhere in small ways. Parents, teachers and school chums can be influences for good or bad. And so can entertainers. In particular, a bad message should never be allowed to go without comment by those who know better.

"Not that the Rudolph song would turn a good kid into a criminal. But there are many influences that contribute to a child's moral character and this is one of the bad ones. People get into trouble with the law for all sorts of reasons, and bullying is one of them. During my time on the force, I ran into many guys who weren't really bad, but they took a wrong turn because they had the same lack of moral center as those reindeer of Johnny Marks. I figure one of my missions in life is to spoil Rudolph for as many people as I can."

He turned to Kit, "Did you really hear Rudolph on the radio?"

CHAPTER

Spring turned into summer and with summer came the berry season. First came strawberries, then raspberries and finally blueberries.

At the Tuesday duplicate game, Phil was playing with Corey. They were following a slow pair. It felt as though they were spending more time waiting than playing bridge, but Phil didn't mind as much as he usually would. Corey was good company.

"I've been thinking about blueberries," said Phil.

"Mary tried picking last week. It was too soon. It's been warm since then. They should be good by this weekend. Would you like to go berry picking?"

"Do you ever pick out by the railroad bridge?" asked Phil.

"Once in a while. The picking is not as good there as it is up north."

"When I was a kid, we used to go exploring on the rocks west of the trestle," said Phil. "I haven't been out there for years. Would you consider picking in a second-best patch this Sunday?"

"Sure," she said. "It might even be better for the next week or so. The berries start to ripen a few days earlier here in the Carter Valley than they do on the highlands further north."

* * * * *

It had been some time since berry picking had held any appeal for Phil. Now he was off, for the first time in years, to pick blueberries. He planned to swing by Corey's at half past one and be out on the rocks when the afternoon freight went through.

He intended to clock the train from the time he heard it to the time it came through the rock cut and onto the bridge.

Phil was not sure why he was doing all this, or what he hoped to discover. He had not even mentioned it to Dan Cogan, because until he clocked the train, he couldn't be sure of hearing the train for more than a second or two before it appeared. He remembered it being more than that, but it was a thirty-year-old memory, so he kept it to himself. He and Dan had not talked about Elsie since they struck out with Kit a month before.

Phil's thoughts turned to Corey. For much of the time that Corey had been playing duplicate, Phil had been aware of her only as a reasonably competent novice player. When she first emerged from the novice section, she was better that he expected her to be, but was still not very good.

In the past few months, he had played with Corey at the club a couple of times and they played a few home games with Dan and Christine. As he came to like and respect her, he also came to realize she was a very attractive woman. She was not a bad bridge player either, and she was improving. Phil enjoyed playing with her. This would be their first outing unconnected with bridge. Corey came from a long line of berry pickers and could not understand why everyone did not head for the hills in blueberry season.

Once out on the rocks, Phil was a little surprised to discover how much he was enjoying himself. He had only half as many berries as Corey, who kept assuring him this wasn't real berry picking. The berries tasted good and he liked roaming, discovering little patches of large berries and rediscovering a landscape that was familiar from his teen years. The main purpose of the expedition retreated to the back of his mind and he almost missed the faint whistle of the train at the crossing. Oak Ridge blocked most of the sound and if part of his mind hadn't been listening for it, he'd have missed it entirely.

Phil glanced quickly at his watch and ran towards the canyon in order to be able to listen for the train as it came through the cut. He needn't have run. It was a full minute before the train whistled again, as it always did on the approach to the bridge, though the whistle was oddly muffled by the moss-covered walls of the rock cut. After the second whistle, it was ten seconds before he could hear the low rumble of the diesel engines and another twelve seconds before it finally appeared.

Phil sat and watched the train cross the canyon. The lead engine was completely across the trestle in eighteen seconds from the time it had come into sight. Phil estimated it would take just under two minutes for a person to run across the bridge, so even if Elsie missed the whistle at the crossing, and was halfway when the train whistled just before the rock cut through Oak Ridge, she could have turned around. With the train slowing as it crossed the trestle, she would have had about 45 seconds to get back. With the train at her back, she should have been able to get close enough to the edge of the ravine to make a safe jump.

"Did you always want to be an engineer?" Corey sat down beside Phil.

Phil was startled. He had been so absorbed with timing the train that he had forgotten he had company. "The way you took off out of the berry patch, I thought maybe you'd stepped on a hornet's nest."

Phil had not mentioned his ulterior motive in coming out here and was tempted to tell a small lie to explain his behavior. Unaccustomed to telling lies, nothing came immediately to mind, so he opted for the truth, "I wanted to see how long you could hear the train before you could see it."

"Now why would you want to do that?"

"Dan told me about talking to Angie. Remember how Angie said that on the day Elsie died, neither she nor Kevin heard the train until it actually came into sight?" asked Phil.

"It doesn't surprise me. When a smoke alarm goes off, it kind of pulls you into it. As long as it's on, you don't pay attention to anything else."

"I know, but if you were thinking about crossing a railroad bridge and you knew it was train time, you'd probably hear the train."

"I might. But smoke alarms and train whistles are similar sounds. I imagine it would depend on how worried I was about my house burning down. But what is it with you and Dan? Why don't you let that poor woman rest in peace?"

"Dan thinks Clayton has been acting a little odd since Elsie died and I have to agree."

"Honestly, you men!" said Corey. "The guy loses his wife without the least bit of warning and you expect him to act normal? I think he did very well. I never noticed any odd behavior."

"That's part of it. In the days after her death, he put on a long face, but he didn't seem stricken. In fact, if anything, he seemed smug. And then, months later when you would expect him to be getting over it, that's when he went off his food. He went kind of dull, like you might have expected just after she died."

"People aren't textbooks. But what's that got to do with whether you can hear the train before you see it?"

"Probably nothing. But as long as there's things that don't add up, I can't get rid of the suspicion that Clayton might have somehow had a hand in it."

"Now isn't that the limit! Clayton's nowhere near the place and he made her promise not to cross that bridge and you think he's somehow responsible for her death just because Angie and Kevin didn't hear the train."

"It isn't just the train. See how far it is across to the house. Do you think you could hear that alarm all the way over here, let alone back at the pond?"

"Clayton explained that, but I guess Dan didn't tell you. Clayton put a speaker up on the outside of the house because..."

"I know that," interrupted Phil. "But even with a speaker on the outside of the house, it would be really faint over here — if you could hear it at all. But that's something we'll never know. I don't intend to camp out here until Clayton burns another roast."

"Do you want to know badly enough to take a Friday off work?"

Phil looked at her quizzically. "You're not proposing to set off that alarm?"

"Not me," said Corey, "but my sister comes out here every Friday to clean. Clayton usually finds something to do in town or up in the Soo to stay out of her way. In other words, she always has the house to herself. She might do it."

Mary had no objection to setting off the smoke alarm. Five days later Phil and Corey were picking blueberries again. The agreement was that, as close as possible to three o'clock, Mary would smoke a cigarette directly under the smoke alarm. Phil was at the edge of the canyon at 3:00 p.m. and Corey was back at the pond. When the alarm went off, it was faint but distinct. Phil walked slowly back to the pond, removing his shirt as he went. It had been cloudy when they arrived, but the sun was out now and it was getting hot.

"Did you hear it?" he asked.

"I think so, but I couldn't be sure. It was so faint I wondered if I was actually hearing it or if my imagination was making it up. One thing's for sure, if I hadn't been listening, I wouldn't have heard a thing."

Corey was accustomed to picking blueberries while in a blueberry patch, but since her job was to sit still and listen, she had spread a blanket on the moss and was sunning herself. The usually business-like Corey looked up languidly and Phil's knees got weak. The sun and the heat were making him dizzy.

Phil dropped to his knees beside Corey. He leaned down and kissed her. She kissed him back.

"You took your time," she said.

They made love in the blueberry patch.

"Will you come home with me tonight," asked Phil.

"Yes, I will. And if you want me to stay for a second night, I might do that too. But just so you know, I've got a pregnant daughter at home and until her situation's settled, she's my first priority."

"Let's pick a few blueberries to have on ice cream tonight before we go to bed," said Phil.

They didn't stray very far from one another. Phil's attention was divided between picking blueberries and watching Corey picking blueberries. Many years had passed since his one serious relationship. Sheila Hoover was the sexiest woman Phil had ever met. When he started going out with her, he knew she was also involved with a guy from Thessalon. Then she told him her relationship with the other guy was over and they got very serious very fast. She got pregnant and they got married. Their child died in childbirth and their love cooled. They separated less than a year after they had married.

After Sheila left, Fran informed him that the child wasn't his (the birth was not premature as she had led him to believe). Phil did the math and realized she was right. Sheila must have decided that if she were going to settle down, she would rather do it with him than with her Thessalon boyfriend. With the baby out of the picture, her reason for settling down had disappeared.

He thought about Elsie. She'd been different from Sheila. Her polar opposite in almost every way, in fact. He'd been close to Elsie, but during the time they were both unattached it had not occurred to him that they could be lovers. She was his 'road not taken,' except that in the Frost poem, the poet looks hard at both roads before choosing. In his own case, he hadn't even noticed there was a fork in the road until he was well past it. He might have remained unaware, were it not for a comment from Elsie during a sit-out at the bridge club, just a few months before her death.

"I do think, sometimes, that the high regard we have for love in our culture is misguided," said Elsie. "It's a severely flawed way of selecting a mate. Take you and me. We're both attracted to the wrong people. For your one try at marital bliss, you chose the hottest babe on the North Shore. It lasted a year, if I remember correctly. In the case of me and Clayton, we've lasted longer, and I still have hopes for the future, but the bickering is getting worse.

"With you," she continued, "I always feel comfortable. A little bored perhaps. But comfortable. Societies that arrange marriages just might have the best system. I've never been attracted to you or you to me. Nevertheless, if we were thrown together and told to make the best of it, we might be disappointed for a while but I think eventually we'd be as happy as pigs in shit."

Corey was not like Sheila or Elsie. There was something different about his attraction to Corey. He was not sure what it was. He just knew he wanted to hold her close. He went over to where she was picking and looked in her basket. "We'll never eat all those tonight," he said.

"Let's go then."

They went back to where the blanket was still laid out on the moss between two patches of blueberries. They started to fold it but somehow got all tangled up and made love again.

Phil had intended to report to Dan. Instead they went back to Corey's where she changed and told Angie she was on her own for supper, and she should not wait up for Corey to get home (leaving Angie in a state of shock). Then they went down to Bruce Mines for a late supper at the Bavarian, then back to Phil's for blueberries and ice cream, then to bed.

Neither slept soundly but both slept well. They woke up with the sun and talked for an hour about life and love and bridge. They showered together, but just to get clean, and they mainly kept to that plan.

CHAPTER 23

It was still early morning when Phil called Dan. "How do you feel about company for breakfast?"

"Maybe you've forgotten," said Dan. "My breakfast menu consists of hot mushy shredded wheat biscuits followed by coffee."

"This morning, the mushy biscuits will be covered with a thick layer of fresh wild blueberries. See you in twenty minutes. Corey will be coming too." Phil hung up before Dan had a chance to respond.

Christine had been planning a day of sketching out on the point at Thessalon. She sensed that breakfast with Phil and Corey would be more interesting and decided to make it an afternoon of sketching instead.

Breakfast, as promised, was mushy shredded wheat with blueberries and brown sugar and then milk poured over everything.

"How was it?" said Dan to Phil. "I know you're not a fan of hot shredded wheat."

"It's pretty hard to spoil blueberries," said Phil.

After coffee was served, Phil announced, "Corey and I went berry picking last Sunday out on the rocks by the railroad bridge. I heard the train whistle at the Brock Road crossing about a mile east of the trestle. It took a minute and a half to get to the bridge. The whistle at the cut was quite clear."

"That sounds like something that needs to be explained before we can put this matter to rest," said Dan.

"We went back out there yesterday," said Phil. "Mary Garson, as we'd arranged, lit up under the smoke alarm at three p.m. The sound was weak but distinct at the edge of the canyon, just barely audible back at the pond."

"That makes two things that require an explanation," said Dan.

"What about Elsie not wearing a watch?" said Christine. "Does that require an explanation? If I was going to cross that bridge, I'd certainly have a watch, either on my wrist or in my pocket."

"As would all of us," said Phil. "But Elsie was a special case. She lived by that bridge all her life. She knew that even though it's called the four-thirty freight, you couldn't set your clock by it. Knowing the precise time wouldn't guarantee her safety. The whistle where the track crosses Brock Road would be more reliable than knowing the time. Better yet would be laying a hand on the rail. Best of all would be to put your ear to the rail."

"Train sounds from the tracks? Are you sure it's not an urban myth? Did you ever try it yourself?"

"Just to see if I could feel anything. The track definitely comes alive when the train's coming. I never tried to put a time on it." Phil paused briefly and then continued, "I do have one more item that's in need of an explanation — the sound of the smoke alarm was described by both kids as fuzzy around the edges. The train sounds have a different quality coming through that rock cut where all the rocks are covered with moss, but I would never describe it as fuzzy. I've been wondering if there's any atmospheric condition that would produce that effect."

"I must have heard the same sound as the kids," said Christine. "There was so much going on I didn't pay attention to the odd quality of the sound. But the few minutes from the time the alarm started until I saw Elsie leap from the bridge is imprinted on my memory, including details I didn't pay attention to at the time. I can play the scene as though it were a movie on tape." She went into a trance for a full minute. "... yes it does sound odd ... wait..." She suddenly got very excited. "I think I may know what it is. Are you all familiar with white noise?"

"What's going on here?" said Phil accusingly. "Did I black out or just nod off to sleep?"

"Sorry about that," said Dan. "Christine was a third witness to Elsie's fall from the bridge. She told me in confidence and at the time I didn't think it added enough to what we already know to get permission from her to tell you about it."

Before Dan could explain further, Corey returned to Christine's question. "I thought white noise was just background noise you didn't pay any attention to."

"In a way that's true," said Christine. "The thing about white noise is that even though it seems to stay in the background, it affects how clearly you hear other things. Effectively, it's the opposite of a hearing aid. When I first got my own apartment in Toronto, I couldn't sleep. I heard every car horn, every shout, every banged door, loud music and television program. I got a little white noise generator and slept like a baby to the sound of falling water. All those city sounds were still there but were much softer and less intrusive."

"Do you have it with you?" asked Dan. "We could do a test and you could compare notes with the kids."

"It's in a closet in Toronto."

"Maybe we don't need it," said Phil. "Every so often the Prof does a training seminar on steam, to keep the crews on weekend or night shifts from blowing up one of the boilers. He always does a white noise demonstration, mainly to get our attention. He cracks a steam valve so there is just enough steam released to make a hissing sound that doesn't seem all that loud. It mimics the effect of a white noise generator. Then he keeps on talking and you can't make out a word."

"I didn't know you worked shifts," said Christine.

"Only when we get a big order, which is not the case this weekend. We'd have the place all to ourselves. There's an old diesel tractor that's used for moving pallets of bricks out in the yard. It has that typical diesel sound. Nobody would ever mistake it for a train but it might be close enough you could judge whether the odd quality of the sound of the train was from white noise."

"Let's do it," said Corey. "I'll call Angie."

"Will the boilers be on?" asked Dan.

"The main job of the boilers is to keep the drying shed warm. No weekends off for the boilers."

The demonstration was short and bittersweet. An hour later, they gathered in the drying shed, which was three stories high and twice the size of a large barn. Phil started the tractor and left it idling outside the shed. Then he opened a steam valve just enough to produce the typical hiss of steam without drowning out the sound of the tractor.

"Yes," said Kevin.

"Yes," said Angie.

Christine just nodded with a stricken look on her face.

After Angie and Kevin left, hand in hand, Dan crouched down on the floor, shaking his head. "I talked through the mystery of Elsie's death with Jonesy, right after it happened. We solved nothing and, as the weeks and months went by, it felt as though we weren't going to learn any more. It's been almost a full year. In the past few months, we've learned there were three witnesses. What we learned from them made it clear that Clayton was responsible but not necessarily to blame."

"That takes me back to grade six and Miss Cameron," said Phil. "I was a shy kid but not so shy that I couldn't point out an occasional error by our teacher. Miss Cameron didn't like being corrected with the result that one day I had to stay after school and write on the blackboard, one hundred times: *sophistry is a subtle, tricky, superficially plausible, but generally fallacious method of reasoning.*"

"This isn't a joking matter," said Christine.

Phil was opening his mouth to defend himself when he felt a knuckle in his side. He took the hint.

"It is definitely not a joking matter," said Dan. "What we've learned is that Clayton did several things which made the accident possible but which could have been motivated by a desire to be considerate and helpful."

"Such as putting a speaker on the outside of the house so that Elsie would hear the smoke alarm if it went off when she was out in her garden," said Corey.

"Such as a car horn signal, to let her know when he was leaving for town," said Christine.

"Exactly," said Dan. "In both cases, his intentions could have been malicious or innocent. The difference between those things and white noise is that it is difficult, perhaps impossible, to come up with an innocent explanation for white noise. It now seems highly likely that it was white noise that changed the sound of the smoke alarm and suppressed the sound of the train. If that's the case, then we have evidence of malice aforethought."

"I'm not sure I see the difference," said Corey.

"Okay. Let's take the smoke alarm with an outdoor speaker. That's suspicious. It lured Elsie to her death. And we know that Clayton was the person who amplified the alarm. But he has a reasonable explanation. Even if we don't believe him, we have no evidence that he had any reason other than the one he gave.

"White noise is different. There are constructive uses for a low-powered white noise machine like Christine's, but I defy you to find an innocent reason for using a white noise machine with enough power to erase the sound of an approaching freight over an area of ten to twenty acres on the other side of the canyon from the old Hamilton place. We have enough pieces that we should be able to make sense of this puzzle. Let's give it twenty four hours and then get together again and compare notes."

"Why do you want us?" said Christine. "You're the detective."

"A detective who's capable of tunnel vision," said Dan. "I've started to put together an overall picture, but I don't want to say too much until you've formed your own thoughts about it. Think about everything we know from two points of view. On one side, try to explain it all away. On the other side, look at the same evidence assuming Clayton's responsible for Elsie's jump. Then see which fits better. Also, if he did it, how did he do it and why did he do it and can we prove he did it?"

"Don't you need physical evidence?" asked Phil.

"Like a white noise generator?" said Christine.

"Or a powerful amplifier," said Phil.

"Physical evidence is important. Not always critical, but probably necessary in this case," said Dan. "Just one word of caution. We may end up confronting Clayton and trying to get him to confess. He's more likely to confess if he's unprepared, so don't do or say anything that might get back to him. I'm planning to go up to the Soo this afternoon. I want to find out what attachments Radio Shack has for their toy computers. Can you come back tomorrow night for supper? The first of my corn is ripe. We'll have some corn on the cob and then see if we can't figure out what Clayton did or did not do."

In the afternoon, Dan went up to the Soo. It was well after dark by the time he left to return to Pemberton. As Dan drove home, he reflected on his position in this business with Clayton and Elsie. He was no longer a policeman, but he could still go down to the station and poke around if it came to that.

When Dan retired, he resolved that the only detecting he would do would be at the bridge table. The department offered a consulting contract, but Dan wanted a clean break. If he did any consulting, he wanted it to be unofficial. That way, he thought, it would be less likely to turn into a real job. In the meantime, he became quite serious about bridge. In fact, at the time he retired, he had thought that he might have enough good years left to become a really good player — one to be reckoned with at the national level. But while the game was easing him into retirement, it had not yielded as easily or as quickly as he had planned. He improved by playing with the best players in the club and by doing a lot of reading. He had become one of the better players in Algoma, but when he went to the big tournaments and met the top players in Canada and the States, he still fell short. They bid better, played better and defended better. Their edge might not be evident over the course of a few deals, but in the major knockout events where you played sixty-four hands against one other team, the difference was decisive.

Dan had gone to the most recent Spring National with Clayton and the Stinsons. Clayton had talked them into it by offering to take care of the hotel accommodation and entry fees. If Dan had three top players for teammates, then he might have done better, but the same could have been said for any of the others. Clayton was the weak link in their foursome. Clayton might not agree, but he had played in luck, for the most part, so he had not held the team back. Fran was a careful, thoughtful player and played well the whole time — a good person to have at the other table; she didn't create many swings but she seldom gave anything away. In that partnership, Phil created the swings. His play was not as good technically as Fran's, but his table presence was tops. At the club, he usually knew who was holding the high cards or who had a long suit or a void. The body language of club players told a great deal if you were observant, remembered individual quirks, and interpreted it all correctly. Phil hadn't much practice in reading top players, so his table presence did not give him the same edge against strong competition. In fact, Phil had assumed that part of being a top player was the ability to give nothing away, so he was a little surprised to come away from that tournament with the feeling that even very strong players gave out little bits of information if he could just learn to read the signs. The big event at the Spring National was the Vanderbilt Knockout teams, which attracted the best players on the continent. The Pemberton team would have to be very lucky to get through the first round. They didn't have to play in the Vanderbilt — there were lower rated events starting at the same time.

The decision was easy. They had not traveled all the way to Texas to play in a secondary event. In the Vanderbilt, they were one of the lowest seeds and were therefore assured of starting against one of the top teams. They were delighted to draw the team headed by the legendary Oswald Jacoby, who was semi-retired but still a formidable player. His teammates were Kaplan, Kay, Pavlicek and Root. The Pemberton team played well, but the gap widened gradually so that by the fourth quarter they were out of contention. Overall, the tournament was both humbling and exhilarating. Dan returned to Pemberton determined to improve, but no longer confident he could become one of Canada's best.

The problem at hand was also humbling. Dan had been uneasy about Elsie's death, almost from the beginning, but there was nothing concrete to justify that feeling — it came from a sixth sense that he had developed over the years. It was usually just a suspicion that something was hidden. This sense sometimes led nowhere. But it kept his antennae up. He knew he would recognize a clue that was relevant to a particular case.

Now Phil and Corey had come up with more information and Christine had added a key observation. He had an overall picture, but he still didn't know how to tie everything together. This was much better, however, than vague feelings of unease.

He would try to determine whether Clayton was a stage manager who should go to jail or whether his involvement was incidental. Dan's sixth sense nagged at him when there was more to an event than there appeared on the surface. Dan had many times been told a story that felt either untrue or incomplete. Sometimes probing revealed criminal activity and sometimes it just revealed a harmless secret. Dan did not admire Clayton, but he liked him and he had a faint hope that at the end of the process he would be able to conclude that even if Clayton had behaved badly, he was not a criminal.

As Dan turned into his driveway, his headlights caught movement in the corn in his garden. He drove past the house and swung into the backyard so that his headlights played directly on the corn patch. He jumped out of the car and sprinted across the lawn, just in time to see a furry ringed tail disappear into the darkness.

Dan's first thought was of Rocky, but Christine was up north and not expected back until the next day for supper. Nevertheless, it was clearly raccoons. Just a few stalks had been pulled down, so they must have just arrived. If they only took what they needed, he wouldn't mind sharing, but raccoons operated on the cob-is-sweeter-on-the-next-stalk principle. They would pull down a cob, strip back the husk, eat enough to ruin the cob, and then move on to a better cob.

Dan had developed a varied approach in his defense against raccoons. Just about everything he had read about and tried had worked for a while and then failed. He now used three of the best approaches in combination.

He went into the house and got a portable radio, a cigarette and a footlong holder that he had prepared for this occasion. On his way out, he grabbed a lawn chair and went to the far end of the patch where he sat down in the chair, lit the cigarette, put it in the holder and placed it on the ground. The holder was clamped onto a stand, which held the cigarette sloped down at an angle of 45 degrees. If the coons were not offended by the burning cigarette, then maybe they would smoke it and he would get them the slow way. He then tuned the radio to CPRB, whose strident commercials, even late at night, were offensive enough to keep the raccoons from carting off the radio. Finally, he took off his pants and deposited his shorts on the chair in the hope that his sweat smelled sufficiently manly to send the raccoons off to someone else's garden.

He put his pants back on, sans shorts, and returned to the house. The corn was just beginning to ripen. He should have been expecting raccoons, but there had been no problems last year so his vigilance had relaxed. Dan surveyed the kitchen and wished that he had cleaned up before he left for the Soo. The living room was a mess too. The house had been too small for a family of four. Now it was too large, though Christine and Rocky had temporarily filled the empty spaces. Maggie Barker came in once a week, usually on Fridays, to clean up for the weekend. When Christine had moved in, Dan had thought the routine might change, but Christine was not much better at housekeeping than Dan. So Maggie, though she disapproved of wild raccoons in the house, continued to come once a week. She had arranged to make it Sunday this week. Dan took another look at the kitchen and decided to leave it. Make Maggie feel needed, he thought.

THE PEMBERTON CHRONICLE

Friday, August 5, 1983

THE JAY'S NEST
by Jane Seabrook

North dealer
Neither Vul.

Dummy (Linda)
- ♠ A 7
- ♡ K 9 3 2
- ◇ J 10 8 5 2
- ♣ Q 5

West (Rose)
- ♠ K Q
- ♡ Q 10 8 7 4
- ◇ K 9 6
- ♣ 10 6 2

East (Kit)
- ♠ 10 9 5 4 3 2
- ♡ A 6
- ◇ 7
- ♣ K 8 7 3

South (Jay)
- ♠ J 8 6
- ♡ J 5
- ◇ A Q 4 3
- ♣ A J 9 4

West	North	East	South
	pass	pass	1NT
pass	3NT	all pass	

Opening lead: ♡7

Linda McFadden and I had an accident on this deal. Linda used to play KS with Andy, so she likes the weak notrump. She doesn't get to play it much now that Andy's gone, so I always play weak notrump whenever we play together. I suspected something was wrong when Linda started with a pass and then raised my weak notrump to game.

After the dummy came down, I counted tricks and saw it wasn't completely hopeless. When I was learning to play bridge, I couldn't count tricks to save my soul. Now I can't see what my problem was.

On this deal, after a heart lead to Kit's ace and a heart back to dummy's king, I counted one trick in spades, one in hearts, five in diamonds, if the finesse worked, and two in clubs, whether the finesse worked or not. That came to nine tricks and my contract. If the diamond finesse didn't work, I would need three tricks in clubs, so I would have to finesse twice and find both the king and the ten onside. You can see, if you look at all the hands, that I was making a plan where I would lose one spade, two hearts, one diamond and one club for down one.

Of course, looking at all the hands, you can see that even though the diamond finesse is off, I could get two tricks in spades if I just played ace and another. However, there was no way I was going to do that. I was just thanking my lucky stars they started with two rounds of hearts rather than spades.

If you had told me that I was going to make three overtricks on this hand against one of the best pairs in the club, I would have been amazed. If you'd shown me their cards, I would have been incredulous. In fact, the only thing that would have surprised me more was if I'd gone to a séance and spoken to my dear mother and it was she who told me I was going to make three overtricks. She's been dead these sixteen years and never played a hand of bridge in her life.

Once I made my plan, I called for a diamond to take the finesse. Of course I should have called for the diamond jack, but before I could correct myself, Kit followed suit, so I played my queen and Rose played the six. When the diamond queen held the trick, I got a little surge of hope until I realized that with The Duck on my left, it didn't mean a thing.

She is quite a good player, really, but you might say that ducking is her Achilles heel. She is willing to tread where even a fool wouldn't rush in. With most players, if a finesse works the first time, you can pretty much count on it working the second time. With the experts, you can't be sure because sometimes they win and sometimes they don't. Then there's Rose, who always ducks, so if a finesse seems to work, you know she must have the king.

Without further thought, I played a low diamond to make her take her bloody king. Well, she just sat there. I waited, patiently at first, but then I got to wondering what she could possibly be thinking about. Finally, it hit me — she didn't know who had the ace and was afraid to play her king for fear that her partner had started with ace double and would have to overtake. Of all the bridge players in Pemberton, Kit was the least likely to be understanding if she played her king under his ace. Once I realized this, I was on tenterhooks, but I stayed just as composed as could be so as not to let the cat out of the bag.

After an eternity, she played low and dummy's jack held the trick. I called for a diamond and slapped the diamond ace on the table, capturing her king and played another diamond.

I try very hard not to gloat but sometimes a little bit of gloat seeps out. Once she made that mistake in diamonds, Rose just fell apart. With the lead in dummy and the last diamond ready to cash, the remaining cards were:

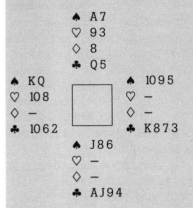

```
          ♠ A 7
          ♡ 9 3
          ◇ 8
          ♣ Q 5
♠ K Q                 ♠ 10 9 5
♡ 10 8                ♡ —
◇ —                   ◇ —
♣ 10 6 2              ♣ K 8 7 3
          ♠ J 8 6
          ♡ —
          ◇ —
          ♣ A J 9 4
```

Kit raised his eyes to the great bridge player in the sky when I dropped Rose's king and then seemed to lose interest in the defense. After pitching three spades, he decided, as I played the last diamond from the dummy, that it must be time to pitch a club. Rose also discarded a club, so now, with the finesse against the king working and the ten dropping, I had four club tricks.

When I was a novice, I played every hand out to the last trick. Then, after a while, I learned to say, "And the rest are mine." Still later I would say, "These are mine and the last two are yours."

This last was just a phase I went through. I quit doing it when I realized there's no benefit in not giving your opponents a chance to make a mistake.

That's why, when the club finesse worked and I found I had four club tricks, I didn't claim saying, "The last trick is yours." And wouldn't you know it? On the fourth club, Rose threw a spade honor, so I took the last trick with my jack of spades. Linda, who hates to miss anything, especially a slam, got a kind of worried look on her face.

"You don't think I should have bid more do you?"

"Once you pitch a club, I get caught in a repeating squeeze," said Rose to Kit.

"Repeating pseudo-squeeze, you mean," said Kit. "Just throw a heart instead of the club and you save two tricks."

It was all academic, of course. We were the only pair in game, so just making the game was a top. The overtricks were window dressing. But what a lovely dress, n'est-ce pas? On the next hand, Rose misplayed a game and tied for bottom with the two novice pairs who made the same elementary error. Which just goes to show you should never scoff at overtricks.

C H A P T E R

Phil and Corey arrived late Sunday afternoon for corn on the cob. The raccoons had not been back, so the first of Dan's crop was still available for human consumption. "Had some corn last weekend from the IGA," said Phil. "It looked good and tasted okay, but it was a little disappointing."

"As soon as the cob comes off the stalk, sugar in the kernels starts turning to starch. Connie used to insist that timing is so important you have to grow it yourself," said Dan. "She would start the water boiling and then pick the corn. That's not so important now, because the breeders have come up with these hybrid varieties that hold their sugar and flavor better, but it still helps. Most of the corn you buy is over-ripe, and even if you get it the day it was picked, it's still been sitting for hours at room temperature. Even the new varieties lose something in that time. My corn is not one of those new extra sweet varieties, but it will knock your socks off."

Christine and Rocky had gone up north the day before and were not back yet. "She said she'd try to get back by 5:30, but if she wasn't here by then, we shouldn't wait."

The corn lived up to its advance billing. Neither Phil nor Corey grew their own corn, but both had eaten homegrown corn before. This was as good as any they had ever tasted. Perhaps better.

"The raccoons almost preempted us," said Dan, as they took their beer out onto the back porch. He told Phil and Corey about his scattergun approach to fending them off.

"Did Clayton ever tell you how he kept the raccoons out of his corn?" asked Phil.

"I didn't think Clayton was much of a gardener," said Dan, surprised.

"He isn't. In fact, I don't think he planted a garden this year. But Elsie was. As you know, Clayton likes fooling around with electronics. He rigged up a beam of light along each side of the garden at raccoon level and a detector at each corner. When the beam was broken by a raccoon entering the garden, it switched on a tape deck that played the barking of a big ferocious dog."

"Did it work?" asked Dan. He had seen too many good-sounding ploys fail to believe it was possible to outsmart raccoons in the long run.

"For two years. In the third year, the raccoons made a raid into the corner of the patch farthest from the speaker. Then they just declined to believe their ears and wiped out the whole patch."

"Clayton must have been fit to be tied."

"No, by then he'd lost interest. He told Elsie that they should just leave corn-growing to the professionals. So she went down to the Co-op and bought an electric fence. She said it wasn't one hundred percent, but they were always able to harvest most of their corn crop."

When Christine arrived around 8:00, she looked as though she had been crying. "Rocky took off and didn't come back," she announced.

"That's terrible," said Corey.

"No, it's not. At least I hope it's not. I wanted him to go. He's too destructive to be a house pet. I've been working on getting him to return to the wild. I cut back on his meals to encourage him to forage. I've been keeping him in his cage when we're in town just to make the town less attractive. But I don't know if he can make it on his own. On our field trips, he's been going off for longer and longer times. This time I stuck around for an extra hour, but he didn't come back to the campsite."

"Where was that?" asked Phil.

"About thirty miles north of Rock Lake."

"So he could make it back here if he had a mind to."

"Yes, but I don't think he will. I've been going to the same area for the past month and he's gotten used to it. If he wanted to come back here, he could have come back in the car with me. I think he may have found a lady friend and decided to stay there."

The first of the evening mosquitoes arrived and they went into the kitchen to sit around the table.

"One of the first things you learn as an officer of the law," said Dan, "is to look at all deaths as though they might be homicides until it's clear that the death was natural or accidental or a suicide. As long as murder is a possibility, the spouse of the dead person is the prime suspect. This creates a difficult situation for two reasons. The spouse is usually the person most hurt by the death. And the spouse is usually not guilty."

Dan's audience all spoke at once.

"I can see where that would create a problem for you," said Phil dryly.

"Why is the spouse your prime suspect?" said Corey.

"Didn't you just say the spouse is usually the one who did it?" said Christine.

"In most cases," said Dan, "there are ten to twenty people you have to consider seriously enough to obtain an alibi. In addition to the spouse, that list includes other family members, friends, co-workers, enemies, plus anybody not listed above that appeared to have the opportunity. Going in blind, the odds of the spouse being guilty is less than 50%. Probably closer to 25%. So the spouse probably didn't do it. But there's no other category on that list that's nearly as likely to be guilty as the spouse."

Dan took a moment to meet all of their gazes, one at a time.

"I've had an uncomfortable feeling about Clayton from the beginning. With no hard evidence, I tried it shrug it off. I came to the uncomfortable conclusion that Clayton was innocent. Even if he wasn't, there was no proof of guilt and there wasn't going to be. Then Phil and Corey discovered that the sound of the train is audible for a minute and a half before it appears and also that the alarm is still audible across the canyon but is much weaker. That raises a few questions without proving anything. Then Christine identified an unusual quality in the sound of the smoke alarm as white noise. That was huge. There was no wind. There was no falling water. In other words, no natural source of white noise. If it was white noise, it was generated with so much power that it could not be an accident and it is quite unlikely there could be an innocent explanation."

"Have you told the police?" said Corey.

"I will," said Dan, "no matter what our conclusions today. But the evidence is still circumstantial. What *has* changed is…"

"Wait," said Christine, "I just figured something out. It fits with what I think you're going to say, but I'd like to say it first so I won't just be an echo."

"Madam," said Dan, with a little smile, which in a less secure person would have been a smirk. "You have the floor."

"When I was talking to Elsie out on the rocks and we heard Clayton give one long and two short honks, it felt like a signal, which it was. The fact that Elsie was expecting him to leave at 4:00 p.m. and therefore got the time wrong was, I assumed, an unfortunate accident. Then, after watching Elsie fall from the trestle, I was overcome by a dreadful feeling of evil. Part of me must have known where the dreadful feeling was coming from, but I clung to the innocent explanation of the horn signal." Christine shook her head.

"For the past twenty-four hours," continued Christine, "I have been trying to think of an innocent explanation for the existence of high power white noise that can mask the sound of an approaching train. No dice. This means that everything associated with the white noise, even if it seems completely innocent, should be re-examined to see if it could be sinister."

"Why?" said Corey. "When I buy a basket of peaches, I feel them to see if they're firm or rock hard. If one of them feels a little soft to the touch and it turns out to be a bad peach, I don't automatically assume all the rest are bad."

"You may not assume it," said Christine, "but doesn't the bad peach make you examine the rest of the peaches in the basket."

"No, I just take another basket," Corey paused. "Okay, you've got a point. I take another basket, but I look at every peach in the basket before I take it."

"As you should," said Dan. "Let's back up the point where you felt that peach that was slightly soft to the touch. You picked it up and took a close look because one possibility was that this peach was just riper than the others. That would be a good sign because peaches that get fully ripe without going bad are succulent and flavorful. They're ambrosia. There's no fruit in the same class. Not even fresh wild blueberries. You should buy that basket and two or three more.

"But," continued Dan ominously, "if the peach is soft because it's gone bad, that's something like the white noise we're concerned about — there's no possible good explanation. The best you can hope for is that the bad peach was an isolated case of mistreatment and the rest are okay. More likely, it's a sign of chilling injury and the whole shipment is affected and in a few days will be inedible."

"You mean the peaches were exposed to a frost?" asked Corey.

"Not even close. Chilling..."

"Stop!" commanded Phil. "I'll tell you about chilling injury later," he said to Corey. "One time I asked Dan about chilling injury at the beginning of my lunch hour. An hour isn't long enough for Dan's chilling-injury rant. Let's get back to Clayton. If he did it, how did he do it?"

"Okay," said Dan. "Let's begin with what I found out in the Soo yesterday. We were thinking he might have used one of his computers to switch the smoke alarm on and off," said Dan. "I talked to a kid at Radio Shack and they don't have any sort of switching attachment for the Trash-80. He thought such things might be available, but he didn't know where. That doesn't eliminate the possibility that he used a computer to start the smoke alarm, but it makes it less likely."

"More to the point, does Radio Shack sell white noise generators?" asked Christine.

"No, but he did say that there are lots of articles in electronic magazines on how to make your own. In fact, if you just hook up a speaker to the output of the computer when it's thinking, it sounds like white noise."

"This is a setback," said Phil. "If he made his own, he probably took it apart when he was done. There goes the most damning piece of physical evidence."

"Yes, I thought that Clayton might have a white noise generator lying around, but now that seems unlikely. Actually, I spent some time worrying about how he might have synchronized the sound of the smoke alarm and the white noise."

"Me too," said Phil. "How long did it take you to realize he just had to record the two sounds on a tape and then play the tape loud enough to mask the train sounds?"

"I did think of that after a while," said Dan. "But he was in town. How would he start the tape? I've been assuming he would have used a computer — that would mean finding a switching device somewhere that would work with a TRS-80."

"It wouldn't have to be a computer," said Corey. "There are lots of timers available. Angie hates alarm clocks, so she uses a timer to turn on her radio."

"Of course," said Dan. "My imagination was stuck on high tech. Still, in order to set the timer and then to be in town when the train came, he'd have to know whether the train was exactly on schedule. My understanding is that it could be fifteen minutes either way."

"And he'd have to know how far Elsie was from the bridge," said Christine. "If she'd started across the bridge fifteen seconds later, she could have turned around. On the other hand, if she was right at the bridge when the smoke alarm started, she could have made it across or at least got close enough for a safe jump."

"Maybe he created a situation where an accident *could* happen without really believing it would," said Corey. "What are the odds that the timing would be perfect?"

"Have you won the Lotto recently?" said Phil.

"Don't be silly. It would be easy to do better than the odds of winning the Lotto," said Corey. "Have you ever been up in the tower?"

Phil realized immediately where she was going with this. "Touché. You know I have. From the tower of Hamilton House, you can see the train track as it comes down into Carter Valley."

"How long, from the time it appears, does it take the train to get to the bridge?" asked Dan.

"I don't know, but the train goes pretty slow until it gets down off the ridge. Also, it depends on how many cars it's pulling. The heavier the load, the slower it goes. Probably somewhere between fifteen and twenty minutes."

"So we're still not very accurate."

"On the contrary," said Phil. "The speed of the train depends on the load, not on the whim of the engineer. You can record the time the engine appears, the time it takes to reach two landmarks on the first curve, and the time it reaches the bridge. Do some calculations, and in the meantime keep an eye on your berry picker. Add an appropriate time for her to reach the bridge and then you can set the timer to turn on a tape player to blast out the sound of the smoke alarm plus the white noise."

"A stopwatch will give you an accurate measure of time," objected Christine. "But if you want to know how fast the train is traveling, you have to know the distance the train travels in the measured time. Are you suggesting Clayton walked up the track for ten miles and found a section of track that's visible from the tower and measured it?"

"Not impossible, said Phil. "But not necessary. Let's deal in round numbers for a hypothetical case. Lets say, for three days in a row, you record times. On the first day, the train takes ten seconds to go from the first to the second landmark. From there the train take sixteen minutes to reach the bridge. On the second day, the train takes twenty seconds between landmarks. You don't know the speed of the train, but you do know it is going half as fast as the previous day and you aren't surprised when the train takes twice as long, thirty-two minutes, to reach the bridge. On the third day, the time between landmarks is fifteen seconds. You predict that the train will arrive at the bridge in twenty-four minutes. The only problem is if the train is going faster or slower than usual between the two landmarks, it's unlikely to maintain that same speed ratio all the way to the bridge—once off the mountain and down on the flats, speeds tend to level out. But if you get enough measurements of time between landmarks and corresponding time to the bridge, you can construct an equation that takes that into account. I'm not sure how the math would work, but I'll bet that with enough data you could predict the time to the bridge within five seconds."

Christine shook her head. "By the time you record the times and do the calculations and set the timer, you could look out the window of Hamilton House and wave to the engineer as the train goes by," she said.

There was complete silence for a few minutes and then Christine answered her own objection.

"This could be where the computer comes into it. A good friend in Toronto has a TRS-80. Two years ago I stayed at his place for a couple of months, house-sitting. I played on his computer the whole time. Learned how to program in Basic. I'd need some assistance with the math, but I'm pretty sure I could write a program where you enter a time reading for the train and a guess for Elsie's distance from the bridge and it would pop out a number for setting the timer. Once you took your reading up in the tower, you could get down to the first floor, enter the numbers in the computer, set the timer and be out the door in about five minutes. With practice, I'll bet it could be done in three minutes... maybe less."

There was silence again and then Christine said what they were all thinking. "So Clayton could have done it."

"The operative word, is *could*," said Dan. "We haven't proved he did it. And if he did it, we can't be sure he used this method. But if it came to a trial, the defense would not be able to say there's no method by which Clayton could have gotten the timing right."

"We have circumstantial proof, but no firm evidence," continued Dan. "Even so, my gut is already convinced. I think what clinches it for me is the white noise. Without that, nothing would have happened. I can't think of an alternative to white noise for damping the sound of the train and I can't think of anybody with the means to produce the white noise, other than Clayton."

"What about motive?" asked Phil. "Surely he wasn't in that much of a hurry to lay his hands on her inheritance. In fact, there's something holding up the will, but it doesn't seem to have affected his living style."

"I think he's been going through his personal savings," said Dan, "and he may have borrowed against the expected settlement."

"For motive, what about wounded pride?" said Corey. "He's a guy whose natural walk is a strut. He's a financial advisor whose wife maintained control of her inheritance and paid him an allowance. That would kind of take the starch out of his strut, don't you think?"

"If he did this thing for such a trivial motive, doesn't that make him a psychopath?" said Christine.

"I don't think so," said Dan. "Psychopaths don't have a conscience. Clayton has one, even if it's underdeveloped. His conscience is something like Lady Macbeth's. Hers didn't keep her from plotting the murder of what's-his-name..."

"Duncan."

"Yes, Duncan. But she had enough of a conscience that it gave her bad dreams."

They concluded that Clayton had viewed the whole thing as a game and had been exhilarated at first by his success. Now, despite the financial independence and the freedom to spend as he wished, he missed the woman whom the better part of him had loved. Perhaps his underdeveloped conscience had finally kicked in. Perhaps he was just lonely.

Proving it was another matter. If they were correct, then Clayton had engineered Elsie's death and he was a murderer as surely as if he had pushed her off the trestle. Unless he confessed, however, they just had a theory. There was nothing to take to the authorities.

"What are the chances he'd confess?" asked Corey.

"Not great," said Dan, "but better than you might think. When you confront somebody with evidence you know what they did, they seem to want to confess. And sometimes they do it when it is clearly in their best interests to keep quiet."

"Isn't it just the dumb ones that confess?" asked Phil.

"They're more likely to confess, but intelligence isn't the only factor. Young people are also more likely. And first offenders are more likely to confess than career criminals."

"Clayton's smart and he isn't young, but as far as we know, this is his first murder. So where does that leave us?" asked Phil.

"There's something else," said Dan. "The likelihood of a confession depends on the suspect's state of mind at the time of the interrogation. If he's feeling confident, he's less likely to confess than if he's confused or insecure. If Clayton is determined not to confess, then state of mind won't matter, but if he's on the edge, then something as apparently insignificant as whether he just won or lost at bridge could make the difference."

"Losing can be arranged. I'm playing with him a week Tuesday and I'm due for an off game," said Phil.

"It'd be better if it was him that made the mistakes," said Dan. "And if there are mistakes he doesn't notice, you could point them out in a helpful manner. Maybe we could insert a few hands into the game where we know what Clayton will do and arrange the cards to make his line of play fail."

"Like his pseudo endplay," said Corey. "The decision Elsie had to make was sort of like the decision a defender has to make. What if Elsie's name came up in connection with pseudo endplays?"

"I'm not so sure about mentioning Elsie," said Phil. "If Clayton figures out we're setting him up, he'll get defensive."

"Not necessarily," said Dan. "For most people, the best way to get them to confess is to convince them you already know what happened so they might as well talk about it. Still, mentioning Elsie might put him on his guard."

Dan and Phil discussed ways in which a pseudo endplay could go wrong. Corey was silent for a while. Then she interrupted, "What if it was Katie who made the connection?"

"What connection?"

"Between Elsie and the pseudo endplay."

"He'd never suspect Katie, but we don't want her involved in this."

"What if I could get her to say something without her knowing what she was doing?"

"Well, Lady Machiavelli, if you could do that, it might work. What do you have in mind?"

Corey outlined her plan and Dan agreed. All in all, Corey, Phil and Dan were quite pleased with themselves at having come up with a theory and a course of action. It was Dan who realized that Christine had been silent for a while. She was very pale. "You don't look so good," said Dan. "I guess we're being a little callous. Or is it Rocky?"

"It's not what you think," said Christine. "If I tell you a secret, will it stay in this room?"

Dan knew that a secret known to four people had little chance of remaining a secret, but he and the others agreed.

"The thing is," said Christine, "I feel like an impostor — well, I am an impostor — but when I came to Pemberton that was my business. Now you're my friends and I want to be straight with you."

She paused and they waited. Finally she said, in a low voice, "Clayton is my father."

Corey recovered first. "You poor dear! We've been pretty mean considering we don't even know for certain that Clayton did what we think he did."

"Does Clayton know he has a daughter?" asked Dan.

"No, and if he did this thing, he never will. My mother lived in Bruce Mines in the late fifties and she seduced Clayton, who wasn't much more than a kid at the time. When she discovered she was pregnant, she invented a job at the festival in Stratford and got out of town. At the time, after she left without telling Clayton she was pregnant, she told herself it was because he was too young to be saddled with that kind of a responsibility. Later, she realized there was another reason. She said Clayton was nice enough, but it was all on the surface. He was like a stray cat who'd come around as long as he was fed and petted. Not daddy material.

"She tried to talk me out of coming north because she was afraid I'd be disappointed in him. I told her I'd look him over and then decide whether to make myself known to him. For a while it was fun, kind of like being a private eye. I soon realized I wouldn't have chosen Clayton for my father, but he seemed okay. I knew Elsie would be in the blueberry patch that day from something she said at bridge. I was in the novice section at the time, but I used to hang around and kibitz a few hands in the main section after our game was over. I was going to talk to Elsie and ask her to invite me to dinner. I liked Elsie and I figured anybody who was with her had to be all right. The smoke alarm went off before I told her who I was. After, I had this terrible suspicion and I didn't know what to do. I decided to stick around and do nothing for the time being. I had no idea I'd stay so long."

When they discussed questioning Clayton after the game, everybody wanted to be there. Dan convinced Corey and Christine it should just be him and Phil. "We want to have him outnumbered, but four of us would be intimidating and might make him defensive."

Dan didn't say it, but after Christine's confession, there was no way he wanted her there.

After Phil and Corey left, Christine returned to the subject of Clayton's character. "Do you think Clayton was born bad? Or did he lose his way somehow?"

"You're pretty much convinced he did it, aren't you?" asked Dan.

"I guess I should at least wait to see if he confesses. But deep down, yeah."

"I suppose we're all born bad," said Dan. "At least, in my experience, babies don't have much in the way of a conscience. But most of us have the ability to develop a conscience. It's just the psychopath that's born without that ability. For most of us, what happens after we're born is what makes us good or bad."

"So it's his mother's fault?"

"Can't blame it all on his mother. She must have been a major influence, but I've seen too many bad eggs come from first-prize mothers. Maybe she's the reason he's not an outright criminal because she was a good influence that countered some bad influences. Of course, there's lots of people with a poorly developed conscience who don't get into much more trouble than cheating on their taxes. But special circumstances can remove the restraints on their negative potential. Some ordinary people in Nazi Germany did some really awful things."

"Clayton didn't have a Hitler giving him a free pass," said Christine.

"No, but there are other pitfalls for a weak conscience. Offer an average person one million dollars to kill somebody face to face and he'll refuse. Make it a thousand dollars to push a button that kills somebody on the other side of the world and you'll get some takers. What we think Clayton did is something like that. Doesn't make it right. But it's not quite the same as cold-blooded murder. Keep in mind we only suspect Clayton. It's a pretty damn strong suspicion, but we don't know it for absolute certain."

Christine nodded, albeit a bit doubtfully.

"If he confesses, that'll clinch it for me," continued Dan, "but you might want to keep in mind that there's a phenomenon called false confession, which is amazingly common."

Christine was not quite ready to drop the subject. "If it wasn't his mother..." she waited for Dan to fill in the blanks.

"Of course, family's the most important influence, whether for good or bad. But there are also friends, neighbors, teachers, sports heroes. Books and movies can also be an influence either way, but I especially worry about the ones that romanticize criminals.

"And of course there's cultural influences like that damn Rudolph song that passes off bullying behavior as a perfectly normal response to a red nose. Probably caused a slight weakening of conscience in millions of kids."

Dan paused briefly and then, speaking to what he knew was on her mind, said, "Clayton has good qualities. If you got anything from Clayton, it was just the good stuff. You have a warmth and ease in the way you relate to people — probably got that from Clayton. The fact you're worried you might not be a good person is a sign you've got nothing to worry about. It's only people with a healthy conscience who worry about being a good person."

Mary Garson was serious about spiritualism and did not take kindly to Corey's suggestion that she fake a séance. There were skeptics who believed that Mary faked all her séances. If she did, it was something she had never admitted to anyone — not even to her sister.

Corey had initially been impatient with Phil and Dan for what she felt were frivolous suspicions. Now she was convinced they had good reasons to be suspicious and she was ready to help resolve the matter. Corey was prepared to argue with her sister, but when she presented her idea, Mary agreed immediately. Mary was still immensely gratified to have been remembered in Elsie's will. Mary had been very fond of Elsie — if Clayton had done something wrong, she wanted him exposed.

At the Tuesday game, while they were watching the scores go up on the big chalkboard, Corey asked Katie if she would be available for a few rubbers on the weekend.

"I have two friends who play bridge but have never come out to duplicate," explained Corey. "I thought if you joined us on Saturday night and they discovered you're not nearly as scary as Jay of the Jay's Nest, they might try duplicate."

"Surely you don't think I'm scary."

"Of course not. You're the nicest person I know. But even though you downplay your ability in your columns, you're are clearly a much better player than Carol and Janet."

"How can I refuse! I'd be delighted."

On Saturday night, as the rubber game was winding down at Corey's house, a car stopped out front and a minute later Mary came in.

"Don't let me interrupt," she said. "Corey told me there would be refreshments. I'm just going to have a cup of coffee and one of these chocolate chip cookies and kibitz for a few minutes if that is okay. That's the right word for watching people play bridge, isn't it?

"My goodness," exclaimed Katie. "Do you and Corey ever look alike. I don't think I ever saw you together. And Mary, I don't remember ever seeing you smile before. When you and Corey smile, you look like identical twins."

"Mary was doing a séance tonight," said Corey. "I told her to drop by if she needed to wind down after."

Katie leaned forward eagerly. Though a firm believer in the Ouija board, she had never taken part in a séance.

"Could we have a little séance right now?" she asked.

"It's tiring for the medium," said Mary. "I wouldn't be very good after this evening's session."

"We could make it very short," suggested Corey.

The others joined in and Mary acquiesced. She pulled up a chair to join them around the table. "Usually, in a séance, my spirit guide, Paulo, comes first and then I ask him to bring the spirits of specific people. Generally, Paulo refuses to come twice in an evening, so what I'll do is wait and hope a spirit comes. We won't know who it is until it identifies itself. It helps if you empty your mind and try not to think of anything until the spirit arrives."

"How long will it take?" asked Janet. "I told my husband I'd be home by midnight." She was both skeptical and curious. She wanted to stay, as long as it didn't go too late.

"That depends upon the spirits. We may not contact anyone. One way or another, it won't take a long time."

Corey lit a candle, set it on the bridge table, and then turned out the lights. They held hands around the table and Mary began to hum tunelessly. Mary's features softened in the candlelight and she acquired an ethereal beauty. After what seemed like a very long time, Mary said, "I feel the presence of a spirit."

There were suppressed gasps around the table.

"Who has come?" Mary asked and then responded to her own question in an entirely different voice. "Elsie Hamilton."

The words had come from Mary's lips, but not only was the voice different, she had tripped over the s's in that almost lisp that Elsie used to have.

"Why have you come?" asked Corey.

"I cannot rest."

Katie, getting right to the point, asked the question that almost everyone in Pemberton had asked at one time or another after Elsie jumped to her death. "What were you doing on the railway trestle?"

Although the business of the smoke alarm had gotten into general circulation, some people, including Katie, thought there had to be more to it.

"It was a bridge hand," said the spirit of Elsie Hamilton.

"What's bridge got to do with it?" Katie asked, perplexed.

"A bridge hand."

"Why can't you rest?"

"A bridge hand."

"What else can you tell us?"

"A bridge hand."

The spirit's needle had obviously gotten stuck and they were not going to get any more out of her.

"Maybe you're too tired," Corey said to Mary. "We ought to let the spirit go."

Instead of agreeing, Mary asked, "Do you have a message for Clayton?"

"The hand will return."

"What does that mean?"

"A bridge hand."

Corey lifted Mary's hand and said, "Mary, let her go."

Mary repeated once more in Elsie's voice, "A bridge hand," and then opened her eyes, leaned back and let her hands fall in her lap.

"Did you hear what she said?" Katie asked Mary. "What does it mean?"

"I heard everything," Mary replied wearily. "But it doesn't make any sense to me. It may not have been a true spirit. Sometimes I just pick up on the vibrations in the room, say from the game you were just playing. It may have no meaning at all."

"Maybe when she was finished picking blueberries," said Katie, "she started to think about a bridge hand and didn't notice she was crossing the trestle instead of going down by the path. It would be easy enough to do. The day after I did my pseudo endplay, I got up to go to the bathroom and ended up pulling grass out of the tulip bed."

After a while, Corey got up to serve tea and biscuits with blueberry preserves. Conversation centered on Elsie Hamilton even though the spirit had supplied no new information. Katie was certain, however, that Clayton would be very interested in their séance. When the bridge players left, Mary stayed behind.

"That was very convincing," said Corey, "but why did you simplify the script?"

"I'm not sure. This felt right and I didn't fight it."

"Do you mean that Elsie actually came?"

Mary's lips twitched. "I don't think so. I didn't feel possessed by a spirit — but something was guiding me."

CHAPTER 27

"Clayton! Clayton!" No sooner had Clayton Carmichael entered the hall than Katie spotted him and rushed across the room, "You'll never guess what we did on Saturday night."

Clayton wasn't sure he wanted to know, but he took her hand in greeting. He smiled. "It must have been very exciting."

Katie surged on. "We had a séance and Elsie came. 'Course, she didn't say much, except something about a bridge hand, but we asked if she had a message for you and she said the hand would return."

"What hand?" asked Clayton sharply.

"Oh, she didn't say any particular hand. All she'd say was 'A bridge hand' and she said it over and over, no matter what we asked, so it probably doesn't mean anything. Except when we asked her why she crossed the trestle, she said 'A bridge hand' and I think maybe she got to thinking about bridge as she was coming back from the berry patch and didn't notice that she was crossing the trestle instead of going down by the path. You see, after I did your pseudo endplay, I got so wrapped up in the hand when I thought about it the next day that I went outside and started to weed the tulips without even realizing what I was doing until suddenly I found myself in the tulip bed."

Katie had perfected the art of breathing while she talked so she didn't have to stop to take a breath. There was no point in watching for a break in the flow — either you interrupted or you waited until she wound down.

"I just found out a while ago," said Clayton tonelessly, "that the smoke alarm went off while Elsie was in the blueberry patch. We had two of the dogs in the house, so she probably didn't even think about the train until it came around the bend."

"Oh," said Katie, and paused for a moment. "Well, Mary said it might not really have been Elsie. She certainly didn't say anything about the smoke alarm, so maybe it was just the atmosphere in the room, because we did, after all, play bridge for three hours before we had the séance."

Dan Cogan had arrived at the hall shortly after six. As the director for the evening, he had preparations to make first. He removed Boards 7 and 8 from the set of boards that were to be used for that evening and put them in another case with the club's second set of boards. Next, he took Boards 9, 12, 15, 19, 22 and 26 from the first set, and replaced them with corresponding numbers from the second set. Then he took the cards from the six boards from the first set and made up hands from a sheet on which were written six different deals.

What Dan was doing could have landed him in trouble with the American Contract Bridge League. They have a provision that allows the director to put prepared hands into play, but Dan didn't think this was what they had in mind when they made that provision. Dan was much more worried about carrying off the sleight of hand by which he intended to insert these prepared hands into play.

He needn't have worried. Duplicate players become so accustomed to having the director handle the movement of the boards that they seldom pay any attention when someone announces an irregularity. None of the players from Table 4 noticed when they were handed boards with a higher number than usual.

The boards were shuffled and they were about to begin play when Dan announced that Boards 7 and 8 had not been passed out. "Folks, it looks like a few of the other boards got mixed up from one set to the other, so would everyone hold on for a minute while I straighten it out?"

Dan brought Boards 7 and 8 to Table 4, telling the players to shuffle, and then went around the room moving boards up one table, unobtrusively inserting boards with the prepared hands, telling the recipients that they were already shuffled so they could just go ahead and play.

The Professor was the only problem. When Dan arrived at his table, he wanted to know why Dan was moving the boards himself rather than just telling everyone, starting at Table 4, to pass their boards up one table. Dan repeated that he wanted to switch some of the boards to straighten out the two sets and he didn't want people starting to play until they got the proper boards. It was clear the Professor would have found a simpler solution, but Mac, on his right, opened one heart, so he got down to the business at hand. Clayton and Phil were sitting North-South at Table 3, as prearranged. Corey was East and starting at Table 1, so she arrived at Table 3 at the same time as Board 9.

Board 9
Dealer: North
E-W Vul.

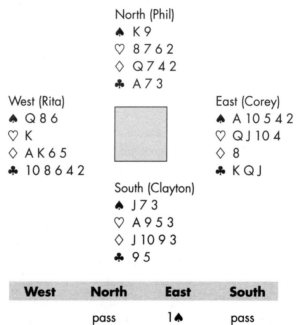

North (Phil)
♠ K 9
♡ 8 7 6 2
♢ Q 7 4 2
♣ A 7 3

West (Rita)
♠ Q 8 6
♡ K
♢ A K 6 5
♣ 10 8 6 4 2

East (Corey)
♠ A 10 5 4 2
♡ Q J 10 4
♢ 8
♣ K Q J

South (Clayton)
♠ J 7 3
♡ A 9 5 3
♢ J 10 9 3
♣ 9 5

West	North	East	South
	pass	1♠	pass
3♠	pass	4♠	all pass

Opening lead: ◊J

The bidding was straightforward. Rita and Corey bid game in spades. Clayton, on lead, played the diamond jack. Corey won in dummy and played the heart king. Clayton immediately returned a spade to cut down on ruffs in the dummy (this was a pseudo endplay situation; against a top player, Clayton might have wondered what the declarer was up to, before leading to the next trick, but he assumed, without even thinking about it, that Corey would not have played the heart king unless she wanted to trump hearts in the dummy). Corey called for the spade six from the dummy. Phil played the nine and Corey won with the ten. Her spade ace dropped Phil's spade king and dummy's queen won the third round. The final result was four spades bid and made, with an overtrick.

Both times the board had been played so far, the result had been a contract of four spades, down one. If Corey had played the spade suit herself (without any illegal preknowledge), she would have won a trick with the ace and then played low towards the queen, hoping that the king was in the South hand. When that guess turned out to be wrong, she would have lost two spade tricks.

Some declarers, noting the drop of North's nine of spades under the ace, would guess correctly to play low from dummy on the second spade trick. They would make their contract, but not the overtrick and thus not score as well as Corey. A few other players would play the heart king at Trick 2, as Corey had done, and if South returned a trump, then they would have a chance to tie with her for a top score. (If North plays the spade king on the trump return instead of the spade nine, it's still possible, though trickier, for declarer to pick up the suit.) One or two such scores would not matter very much to Phil and Clayton, who were assured a near bottom score on this board.

"I wasn't sure how to play the spades," explained Corey to Rita. "I knew I was going to have to knock out the heart ace sometime, so I thought I might as well do it right away and worry about the spades later."

Clayton was annoyed and a little shaken at having been a victim of the pseudo endplay, the more so because Corey appeared to have fallen into it. He was still brooding about this a round later when he faced a similar situation on Board 12.

He knew that he ought to return a trump, but he talked himself out of it. This time declarer really was planning to trump losers in the dummy and Clayton's failure to make the 'normal' trump return cost two tricks.

Two rounds later, both Boards 15 and 16, with Mac at the wheel as declarer, posed the same problem for Clayton. One of these was a genuine pseudo endplay and in the other, Mac was just planning to trump losers in the dummy before drawing trumps. This second deal was not one of the prepared hands. It was a random deal, as if the bridge gods were in on the act, making Phil nervous that they might have overdone it. Clayton guessed wrongly both times. "Bad luck, Clayton," said Phil as Mac left the table. "You never know what Mac's doing."

Clayton was pale and his hands had developed an almost imperceptible tremor. Even when he guessed correctly to return a trump on Boards 19 and 22, he did not regain his composure.

Then they had this deal:

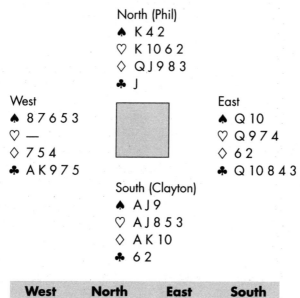

North (Phil)
♠ K 4 2
♡ K 10 6 2
◇ Q J 9 8 3
♣ J

West
♠ 8 7 6 5 3
♡ —
◇ 7 5 4
♣ A K 9 7 5

East
♠ Q 10
♡ Q 9 7 4
◇ 6 2
♣ Q 10 8 4 3

South (Clayton)
♠ A J 9
♡ A J 8 5 3
◇ A K 10
♣ 6 2

West	North	East	South
pass	pass	pass	1♡
pass	3♡	pass	4♡
all pass			

Opening lead: ♣K

After three passes, Clayton opened one heart and the auction proceeded unimpeded to four hearts. West led the club king and then switched to the spade eight. From Clayton's point of view, this was a situation like the pseudo endplay where West would tend to switch to a trump after cashing her club king and noting the club shortness in dummy. Since she hadn't switched to a heart, she probably had something to protect in the trump suit. On a better day, Clayton might have given some thought to the possibility that she didn't have a trump to lead. This was not a good day for Clayton. He played the heart ace and was the second player in the room to make only one overtrick; everyone else made twelve tricks.

A few deals later, the pseudo endplay seemed to rear its ugly head once again.

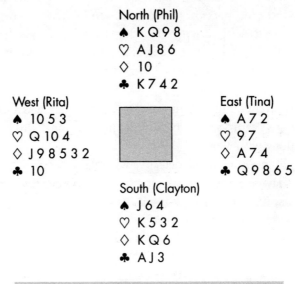

North (Phil)
♠ K Q 9 8
♡ A J 8 6
◇ 10
♣ K 7 4 2

West (Rita)
♠ 10 5 3
♡ Q 10 4
◇ J 9 8 5 3 2
♣ 10

East (Tina)
♠ A 7 2
♡ 9 7
◇ A 7 4
♣ Q 9 8 6 5

South (Clayton)
♠ J 6 4
♡ K 5 3 2
◇ K Q 6
♣ A J 3

West	North	East	South
	1♣	pass	1♡
pass	2♡	pass	4♡
all pass			

Opening lead: ♣10

After Phil's opening bid of one club, Phil and Clayton bid to four hearts and West led the club ten. After East played low, Clayton won with the jack, and immediately led the diamond king. With the pseudo endplay on his mind, it was a natural thing to do, except for the fact that there was no advantage to having West lead trumps. Since Clayton didn't have the heart ten, this was not a two-way finesse situation — he could only finesse towards dummy and it didn't matter whether West made the lead or he did it himself. In other words, this was not a pseudo endplay.

East won with the ace and played a club for West to ruff. West returned a spade to East's spade ace and East led another club for a second ruff. Down one, when most of the field was making an overtrick. "Nice defense," said Phil to Rita and Tina.

Dan and Phil conferred briefly after the game while the scores were going up on the big board. "It certainly feels like he's our man," said Phil. "No incredulity at how many pseudo endplays were cropping up. No anger and frustration when they didn't work out. Just got quieter the whole evening. In fact, I'm beginning to feel sorry for him. If we want him confused and insecure, we've succeeded — he's a basket case."

"I've been thinking I might want to pretend there was another witness to Elsie's death," said Dan. "If I do, just go along with it."

"Go along with what?"

"I might invent a private detective who was following the kids and observed Clayton up in the tower at 4:00 p.m. We can't discuss it right now. I'll use him only as a last resort."

CHAPTER

After the game, Clayton agreed to go to the Donut Shop for a coffee with Phil and Dan. Clayton was almost comatose. There was no difficulty in getting him to come along. They sat in the corner booth at the back.

"Clayton," said Dan, "in the months following Elsie's death, the reason for her crossing the railroad bridge at train time remained a mystery. Then two witnesses came forward and a few months later we discovered there was a third witness. These witnesses were able to explain why Elsie ran across the bridge and why she didn't expect to meet the train. You admitted responsibility for both of these things, and you gave us explanations which, at the time, were credible."

"You don't believe me?" said Clayton, trying to sound indignant, but sounding guilty instead.

Dan had not been confident of obtaining a confession. Now he knew they would. He had conducted many such interviews and he knew the signs. Clayton wanted to confess. He just had to be nudged.

"When you honked your car horn, Elsie took that as a signal that you were heading for town. But more importantly, she took it as a signal that is was 4:00 p.m. and therefore that the train was not due for some time. That, of course, wasn't true. It was 4:23 and the train was due any minute."

"But I explained."

"Yes, you did and we accepted your explanation. At 4:25 the smoke alarm went off. Elsie dropped her blueberries and sprinted for the bridge. It took her just over two minutes to reach the west end of the railroad bridge. The train was close enough that she should have been able to hear it. But she didn't. Neither did any of the three witnesses I've mentioned. Would you like to tell me about the white noise or should I tell you?"

"What white noise?" said Clayton, failing completely to sound puzzled.

"It was the white noise that turned this around for us. The white noise came on with the alarm and both sounds were amplified enough to make them easily audible across the canyon. There's one thing about white noise that's completely incompatible with what you told us. White noise changes the tone of a smoke alarm, making it less alarming rather than more. The main use of white noise is to mask objectionable sounds. What it masked was the sound of the approaching train, which would have warned Elsie to stay off that bridge."

Dan paused and then said, "It's your turn Clayton. Tell us why you did it."

Phil had come along as moral support for Dan, but with low expectations. Phil was the best reader of body language in the Pemberton Bridge Club and by the time Dan commanded Clayton to speak, he sensed that Clayton would confess.

Clayton sat without any sign that he had heard and Phil started to wonder if he'd misread the situation.

Dan continued in a commanding tone, without heat or urgency, "Tell us, Clayton. Confession is good for the soul and yours is in pretty bad shape."

Clayton started to speak and Phil, even though he was expecting it, was still surprised — a confession seemed like too much to hope for.

"Elsie was always funny about her inheritance," he began quietly. "Her old man drilled into her that no matter who she married and no matter how much she loved him, she was not to give up control of the money she inherited. She told me before we got married that the inheritance would always stay in her name and I told her I loved her, not her inheritance. But I never expected she would be firm on that point.

"A few years ago she wanted to take Snowball on the road. She talked me into taking an early retirement so she and I could take Snowball to dog shows all over the continent. He did real well too. The only problem was that we had separate bank accounts. After I retired she supplemented my income, but it didn't much more than cover daily expenses."

"So whenever I wanted to make a major purchase, or even buy something that only cost a few thousand, we had to have a big discussion and she had to be convinced it was worthwhile. There was always a limit on how much we spent in a year, because, until September 1984, we were on a budget of $200,000 per year."

"Sounds like a good budget to me," said Phil. "But what's special about 1984?"

"Elsie had some ten-year GICs coming due then. I see not wanting to cash them early and pay a big penalty, but it would have been easy to borrow against them. Still we got on pretty good until I wanted to go to more of the big bridge tournaments. She wouldn't have objected to me going on my own if I'd just wanted to play with somebody from the partnership desk, but you know how it is at the partnership desk. Sometimes you get somebody really good, but just as often you get somebody who goes to the partnership desk because nobody who knows them will play with them. The only way to be sure you have a good partner is to hire a pro and Elsie couldn't see putting out an extra two to five thousand for a ten-day tournament just so I'd have good partners."

Clayton was becoming more animated and Dan wanted to be sure that he got down to the important details before he began to have second thoughts. "Where did you get the idea on how to do it?"

"It was that damn pseudo endplay. The idea is to make your opponent figure there's a danger where it doesn't exist and to make them choose the path where the real danger lies. The real danger was the train, so all I had to do was to create an impression of a different danger, which I did by setting off the smoke alarm."

"But why would she cross the trestle?" asked Dan. "She lived there all her life. She knew the danger. It would only take a few minutes more to go down by the path."

"That's just it. Since she lived there all her life, she figured the trestle was her personal bridge across the ravine. When we first got married, I had a devil of a time getting her to use the path instead. She knew the train schedules and even though you can't see the train coming down from the north because of the rock cut through Oak Ridge, she could always hear the whistle for the crossing on Brock Road, so she never got surprised by the train."

"So you used the white noise to mask the train whistle," said Dan.

"With Oak Ridge in the way, the sound is pretty faint anyway and Elsie didn't like to admit it but her hearing wasn't as sharp as it used to be. I figured it wouldn't take much. Then by the time the train blew its whistle as it came through the rock cut, the smoke alarm was still going, and I had the volume jacked up, so she probably couldn't hear anything else and wouldn't even have thought about the train until it came around the bend onto the trestle."

"Clayton," said Phil, "I would never have taken you for a murderer."

"I'm not! I loved Elsie. I know it looks bad, but I never thought it would work. What are the odds the timing would be just right for her to be just far enough across the bridge that she couldn't get over or back? I had no idea whether the white noise would work. I never would've laid a hand on her. I just set up a situation where she might decide to do something that I told her time and again not to do. Figured it might teach her a lesson."

Dan and Phil exchanged a glance, neither surprised by the look of barely concealed disgust in the other's eyes.

CHAPTER 29

Dan and Phil agreed to not tell anyone other than Corey and Christine about the confession until Dan had had a chance to talk to Jones. The next morning at 8:10 a.m., as Dan was eating breakfast, the phone rang. It was Katie. "Is it true that Clayton confessed?"

"Where in the world did you hear that?" said Dan.

"Is it true?" cried Katie.

"Yes, it is," said Dan. "Now tell me, how did you hear about this?"

"My cousin Terry called me from Kingston. All she knew was that Elsie's husband confessed something and she thought I'd be able to tell her all about it." Katie's voice was breaking up.

"I'm not free to discuss this until I've talked to Jones," said Dan. "But I cancelled my game with Clayton for this coming Tuesday and told him he wouldn't be welcome at the bridge club until this thing is resolved. Perhaps not even then," he added grimly.

"I thought he was such a nice man. What an awful judge of character I am."

"Don't beat yourself up," said Dan. "Elsie married him. Phil and Fran and I played a lot of bridge with him."

When Christine came down for breakfast, Dan told her about Katie's call. "I don't know how this works," said Dan. "Once in a while a secret seems certain to spring a leak, but then it remains a secret. Most other times, it gets out to the whole town before you can finish a cup of coffee."

"I didn't tell anybody here," said Christine. "But I called my mother in Toronto. She wouldn't have told anybody in Pemberton, but she has a close friend from Bruce Mines who now lives in Napanee."

"Who probably knows Katie's cousin Terry in Kingston," sighed Dan.

The phone rang. It was Fran. "Is there something you'd like to tell me?"

* * * * *

Within a few days, it became clear to Clayton that he was no longer welcome in Pemberton. Some people crossed the street to avoid him. Others walked past as though he was invisible. He decided to move to the Soo until the will was finalized. The Soo is much larger than Pemberton. Easier to be anonymous.

Not easy enough. There were one hundred bridge players in the Soo who knew him by sight. Many people from Thessalon, Bruce Mines, Bar River and Echo Bay went to the Soo to work or shop or dine or go to a movie. To these people, he was invisible. It felt sometimes as though the people who looked right through him outnumbered the strangers to whom he was merely a person they did not know. He had always been gregarious. Now he yearned for anonymity.

The capper, after two months of feeling that everyone was either judging him or pretending he didn't exist, was a chance meeting with Katie Burton. She was, he thought, the one person from Pemberton who would listen to his side. He held out his hand.

"Katie, I am really glad to see you," he said.

Katie kept her hands in her pockets. "Clayton Carmichael, you make me ashamed. I thought you were a good man and a nice man. How could I have been so wrong?"

"I'm not a monster! I never intended or expected the horrible result."

"How could you make Elsie cross the trestle at train time without expecting the worst?"

"It was the timing," he said miserably. "If the train hadn't come through the cut just when it did, she'd have been able to get across or turn around and get back. The chance she'd have no safe option was about the same as getting hit by lightning."

Katie narrowed her eyes further. "Did you also encourage her to go out in thunderstorms?"

"Katie, c'mon, at least hear me out. You're the one person I knew would listen."

"The more fool me." Katie turned on her heel and walked away. Clayton had intended to stay in the Soo until he had his day in court. He changed his mind. Two days later he moved to Toronto.

Clayton was able to remain anonymous in Toronto with one significant exception. The bridge playing community in North America is, in some ways, like a small town. A bridge club in Toronto advertised that they always had a player on standby — come and play whether you have a partner or not. Clayton dropped in on one of their games to see if any of their members regularly went to the Northern tournaments and would therefore be likely to recognize him. He didn't see anybody he recognized or that seemed to recognize him.

He came out for the next evening game, using a fabricated name. He and his pickup partner were clearly the class of the field. Clayton was enjoying himself. After the game, a woman who looked vaguely familiar approached him. He assumed she was going to offer congratulations on his good game and say something welcoming. Instead she said, "Aren't you the guy that pushed his wife in front of a train?"

Clayton didn't go back to that club or any other. He became a recluse. Finally, two years after the reading of Elsie's will, Clayton returned to the Soo for his five minutes in court. One year had passed since his confession and the story of Clayton's part in Elsie's leap was known up and down the North Shore.

Estate law is less prescriptive than criminal law. Disputed wills are settled by a judge using somewhat flexible principles such as *lex non scripta*, which translates as 'unwritten law'. This is usually taken to mean that the judge should be guided by general practice, with some latitude allowing the judge to do what he feels is fair with respect to the rights of the living and the wishes of the deceased.

The executor of the will calculated that under the terms of the will, Clayton should receive $500,000. Clayton felt he was entitled to an amount closer to $2,000,000

Early in the proceedings, the judge asked for an estimate, from the executor, of the increase in value of Elsie's estate during the time of their marriage. This came to $400,000. The judge said Clayton was entitled to half of that. The remainder of the estate was Elsie's to dispose of as she wished. In other words, Clayton could have accepted $500,000 from the executor; he was now being offered $200,000 by the judge.

Clayton's lawyer was flabbergasted. "Your Honor, you must know that we will be appealing this decision. May I ask Your Honor if you were influenced by the unsubstantiated rumors that my client confessed to being responsible for his wife's accident?"

"That would be hearsay and therefore inadmissible," said the judge. "I did have a brief discussion with a retired officer of the law who appeared before me many times and was an excellent investigator with a good understanding of the law. I just asked him one question: Would the evidence of the husband's involvement in his wife's death, which is obviously not sufficient to try him in a criminal court, be sufficient to convict him in a civil trial? His answer was yes.

"At the present time, if a husband is convicted in a criminal court of killing his wife, he inherits nothing from her estate. Wills are a civil matter where rather than proving a crime beyond a reasonable doubt (as in a criminal court), it is sufficient to show that the chances that he did it are greater than fifty percent.

"If the husband were charged and convicted in a civil trial, he would not go to jail but he would get nothing from the estate. This would be breaking new ground in a Canadian court. We do not, at the present time, hold murder trials in civil courts. But Florida estate law is moving in that direction and I'm inclined to think we should too. In any case, I will add that recommendation to my written decision."

"This is blackmail," said the lawyer, under his breath.

"Pardon," said the judge.

"Nothing, Your Honor."

Clayton's lawyer was positive that if they appealed, the judge would be sanctioned. Clayton felt that everybody on the North Shore believed the worst and would continue to believe the worst no matter how the estate decision went. He was an outcast in Northern Ontario and had no desire to appeal to a higher court and have his fame spread further. He accepted the $200,000 and moved to British Columbia.

C H A P T E R

Christine spent most of September and part of October redecorating as promised. Wallpapering was easy. The woodwork was another matter. When she first moved in, she had visions of removing layers of paint on the door and window frames in order to expose the natural grain of the wood, which she would then cover with clear varnish.

Rocky's presence had changed her plans. She used filler to smooth over the marks of Rocky's claws and then put on another layer of paint. Then there was the furniture. Christine refinished and reupholstered. As she neared completion, she became more thorough.

She found herself more reluctant to leave than she had expected. She and Dan had grown very close. Not quite in a father-daughter sort of way, but not in a romantic way either. She promised to visit — perhaps in the spring, for Russell and Katie's wedding. She drove up north of Rock Lake the day before she left, to where she had dropped off Rocky, but he did not appear.

THE PEMBERTON CHRONICLE

Friday, April 20, 1984

THE JAY'S NEST

by Jane Seabrook

South dealer
N-S vul

	Dummy (Rita)	
	♠ Q 7 4 3	
	♡ 4	
	◇ 10 8 7 4 3	
	♣ 9 7 2	

West (Jake)		East (Kit)
♠ A J 10 9 2		♠ 8 6 5
♡ K 8		♡ 9 7 6 5 3 2
◇ A 6 2		◇ Q 9
♣ K J 6		♣ 8 3

	South (Jay)	
	♠ K	
	♡ A Q J 10	
	◇ K J 5	
	♣ A Q 10 (5) 4	

West	North	East	South
			2NT
3♠	pass	pass	3NT
all pass			

Opening lead: ♠J

"Hello, Jay," said Kit, as he sat down, a sure sign he was in a good mood. A sign also that there had been no problem at the last table for which Jake needed a lecture. Rita came back with our coffee and I stirred in the sugar as I sorted my hand and put the club five in with the spade king. Everybody missorts their hand from time to time and I'm no more perfect than the next person.

I made what seemed like a perfectly reasonable bid of two notrump. Jake stuck in a three-spade bid, which was passed back to me. I hate it when these experts come into your auction just because they're not vulnerable. Rita probably didn't raise because she had no spade stopper, so I decided to teach Jake a lesson and bid three notrump.

This turned out very well for Rita and me. "What did you hope to gain?" said Kit in the postmortem. "You're always making bids like that. You don't have enough spades and you have too much defense. Not that you made use of it."

Now isn't that the truth. At least the part about defense. As far as the bidding goes, Jake marches to his own drummer.

Look at all four hands and see if you can make three notrump, after the spade jack lead. I can tell you right now I wouldn't have a chance playing against anyone but an expert.

I won the opening spade lead with my king and since I didn't know I had five clubs, I decided my best source of tricks was diamonds. With no way of getting to the board for the finesse, I just plunked down the diamond king.

It won! When I get a gift horse, I don't look at its teeth. I promptly played the diamond jack, which Jake won with his ace, dropping Kit's queen. Kit glowered. Ducking my diamond king wasn't too surprising. Anybody might have done it. But winning the second round of diamonds required expert logic — when I played the diamond jack, Jake decided I must have started with king-queen-jack in diamonds. So he won in order to play ace and another spade to use up my entry to dummy while the diamonds were still blocked (Kit's play of the diamond nine under my king had looked like the start of an echo showing the nine-five doubleton).

If I held Jake's hand, I might win the first or the third round of diamonds, but never the second. Only an expert would win the second. I just love playing against experts. When Kit's queen dropped, Jake abandoned his plan of knocking out my spade entry and just played his last diamond.

I asked Jake why he didn't play spades anyway in order to have some tricks to cash when he got back in. He said it would have set up two tricks, but then he would have had to pitch at least one of them on the run of the diamonds. He was giving me credit for knowing what to do if, instead, he pitched clubs and hearts on the run of the diamonds. I appreciate the compliment, but if I were defending against myself, I wouldn't be so sure that I would do the right thing.

In any case, he played a diamond instead of clearing the spades. I continued diamonds. Kit discarded his spades to give Jake the count, so Jake knew that I had no more spades. That was more than I knew because I still thought that my club five was a spade (when Kit played the spade five on the opening lead, it should have made me suspicious, but I hadn't noticed). I pitched the four and ten of clubs.

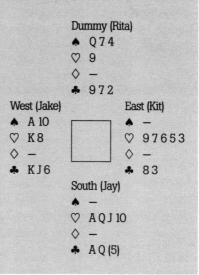

Dummy (Rita)
♠ Q 7 4
♡ 9
♢ —
♣ 9 7 2

West (Jake)
♠ A 10
♡ K 8
♢ —
♣ K J 6

East (Kit)
♠ —
♡ 9 7 6 5 3
♢ —
♣ 8 3

South (Jay)
♠ —
♡ A Q J 10
♢ —
♣ A Q (5)

Now I did something silly. With five tricks in, I should just give up a heart and wait for the last four or five tricks. Just making this contract was going to be a top. The reason I didn't was that when Jake played his diamond ace, dropping Kit's queen, Jake raised his hand in disgust and showed me the heart king just as plain as day. I usually make a point of not looking when my opponents tip their hand and I certainly didn't benefit this time. It gave me the idea, which seemed very clever at the time, that if the club finesse worked, I could then play the ace, get out with my five of spades (clubs) and endplay Jake, forcing him to play hearts to me.

I took the club finesse, losing to Jake's king. Kit said later he gave count in clubs, but by this time, with Kit stewing over there, Jake was not at his best. Even if he had noticed Kit's discards, he would have had to decide whether to believe Kit's count or my discard of the club ten. Actually, I'll bet when he saw my club ten, he just stopped thinking about what I must have because he knows me well enough to know I would never discard the club ten ahead of the club five — that's an expert play and it backfires often enough for the experts. You can imagine how it would work for me.

Fran says I can still make my contract at this point no matter what Jake does, as long as I play carefully. Fortunately, he didn't put me to the test. Since he and I both thought that my ace of clubs was stiff, he decided to return a small club, right after he cashed his ace of spades.

Kit asked him why the hurry to take the spade trick. Jake didn't answer, but I think I know. He wanted to punish me for fooling him in diamonds, so he set up two tricks in dummy that I wouldn't be able to get to. When he played the ace of spades, I had my hand on the club five before I realized it wasn't a spade after all. I put it back, because I didn't want to give these guys the satisfaction of discovering that I had missorted, and pitched a heart instead.

When he returned the small club, my nine of clubs won in dummy and I pitched my heart losers on the spades. A top! I love tops and I'll take them wherever I find them, but I especially love tops against experts.

C H A P T E R

During a long cold winter and spring, Phil and Corey spent a lot of time together. Much of that time in Phil's bed. They had both been celibate for years and were doing their best to get caught up. Phil and Corey got up late on the last Sunday in April. The weatherman was predicting a sunny day with the possibility of record highs. They had brunch while still in their bathrobes and made plans for a short hike north of town. Where they went wrong was changing into outdoor clothes in Phil's bedroom, both at the same time. They didn't get much beyond removing their bathrobes. After making love and deciding there was no need to rush the hiking season, Phil said, "How would you feel about me smoking for a few weeks?"

She sniffed. "I'd boot you out of my bed."

"If I'm not mistaken," said Phil, "this is my bed."

"If you want me to continue coming over here and staying the night," said Corey, "this is my bed."

"Of course. What was I thinking?" said Phil. "This is definitely your bed."

With that settled, Phil returned to the smoking issue. "Why are you so set against smoking?"

"Well, let's see. I have a lover who's clean, healthy and smells good. I could trade him in for a lover who's somewhat more likely to get cancer, a heart attack, or one of many other interesting diseases, and who stinks and never gets completely clean. It's a tough choice."

"You paint a pretty picture," said Phil.

"That's just one side of the picture," said Corey. "Have I mentioned that I used to smoke? This talk of smoking reminds me that lying in bed with a lover is one of the nicest times to light up. You can see my dilemma."

"When I stopped smoking I made myself a promise that after a year on the wagon, I would smoke again for anywhere from a week to a month."

"I'm sure 'yourself' would understand if you explained that you've changed your mind," said Corey.

"My mother used to say that a man who can't keep a promise to himself shouldn't be trusted to keep a promise to anyone else."

"I wouldn't want to contradict anyone's mother, especially yours. But tell me the answer to my next question?"

"...I don't hear a question."

"Answer it anyway." This was not how Corey usually asked a question, but some of Phil's mannerisms were infectious.

"Okay, you want to know why I'd make such a silly promise."

Corey nodded.

"You know that I quit a year ago, and you may have noticed that smoking is one of the few personal topics we haven't discussed. I'm not sure why you didn't bring up the subject, but I know why I didn't. It's because the program I'm on sounds a little nutsy. Basically, the theory is if you promise yourself that after a year you can start again for as much as a month, it makes quitting easier. And when you start smoking a year later, it feels like you won a prize rather than feeling like you're a failure. So you're more likely to stop smoking again for another year."

Corey raised an eyebrow. "Has it worked?"

"So far so good. But back to getting kicked out of this bed of yours. The past six months have been the happiest of my life. From time to time, we've gone a full day without seeing each other and twice we went two days. That's only made the sweet things sweeter. We could pretend the Brickworks sent me down south for a training course. I think we could do a week apart without...."

"Hold it right there, buster. If you must smoke for a week, I want a chance to give you a hard time. Here's how it'll go. You'll do all your smoking at work or here on the back porch. I'll come over every day and make you supper, but every time you come in after a cigarette, you'll gargle with mouth wash. After supper, if I'm in the mood, you'll have a shower before joining me here in my bed."

* * * * *

Phil smoked several cigarettes in the course of the Tuesday game (he was not playing with Corey). Next day at noon, Dan asked him how it felt.

"Great," said Phil. "Well, maybe not quite as great as I expected, but still pretty good."

"Was everybody surprised you were smoking again?"

"No, the only ones to say something were Katie and Fran. I do believe that most of the club didn't even notice I'd quit. Those that did know about me quitting were so used to seeing me with a cigarette over the past twenty years they just switched back to that picture."

"You going to quit again on schedule?"

"Yessir."

* * * * *

Dan was eating breakfast and studying a bridge hand when he heard scratching at the back door. He opened the inside door and looked out through the screen as a large raccoon settled back on its haunches and looked up at him, like a pet waiting to be let in.

Appendix A

Members of the Pemberton Duplicate Bridge Club

Elsie Hamilton Carmichael: Heiress and dog breeder. She died nine months before the beginning of the story in a dramatic and somewhat mysterious fashion.

Clayton Carmichael: Retired insurance salesman and financial consultant. Husband of Elsie.

Kit McCrea: Cab driver with a small independent income. Descendant of the founder of Hamilton Brickworks.

Katie Burton: Author of a weekly bridge column called The Jay's Nest. Her *nom de plume*, Jane Seabrook, doesn't fool anybody. But Katie is always nice and Jane Seabrook is not. So Katie is more comfortable writing under another name..

Fran Stinson Porter: School teacher, club president. Best bridge player in Pemberton.

Phil Stinson: Foreman at the Brickworks. Twin brother of Fran.

Corey Garson Loucks: Widowed mother of three (two of them married). Angie, teenaged and pregnant, lives at home with Corey and is still in school.

Dan Cogan: Retired policeman. Gardener and bridge scholar. Separated from his wife because he came to Pemberton from Southern Ontario to further his career and he stayed too long.

Jim Campbell (The Professor): Stationary engineer and bridge teacher.

Jake Harden: Farmer and local historian.

Christine Williams: Artist from Toronto. For the past year, Pemberton has been her base for sketching field trips both locally and along the shores of Lake Superior north of Sault Ste Marie. Sells paintings in Toronto for exorbitant prices.

Mac: Dentist. Luckiest card player in Pemberton.

Rose (The Duck): Dental technician. Works with Mac but they seldom play bridge together because neither ever knows what the other is doing.

Russell: Welder.

Doc: Family doctor.

C O M I N G   I N   2 0 1 2

Don't miss the next
Pemberton Bridge Club mystery
from Ken Allan

Shades of Gray

Revisit the Pemberton Bridge Club, along with the 'Jay's Nest' bridge columns, from Ken Allan's first novel, *Deadly Endplay*. This time the players face the growing suspicion that someone in their midst is systematically cheating. As Dan Cogan begins to look for evidence, various issues arise: When does dubious ethics become cheating? Can you prove cheating from hand records? And if you can, what should the penalty be? Finally, why do people cheat at duplicate bridge — a game that offers no monetary rewards? There are no easy answers, only various shades of gray.

Master Point Press on the Internet

WWW.MASTERPOINTPRESS.COM

Our main site, with information about our books and software, reviews and more.

WWW.TEACHBRIDGE.COM

Our site for bridge teachers and students — free downloadable support material for our books, helpful articles and more.

WWW.BRIDGEBLOGGING.COM

Read and comment on regular articles from MPP authors and other bridge notables.

WWW.EBOOKSBRIDGE.COM

Purchase downloadable electronic versions of MPP books and software.